MY NORTH STAR

MY NORTH STAR

Bob Partridge

ARTHUR H. STOCKWELL LTD
Torrs Park, Ilfracombe, Devon, EX34 8BA
Established 1898
www.ahstockwell.co.uk

ISBN 978-0-7223-5062-1
Printed in Great Britain by
Arthur H. Stockwell Ltd
Torrs Park   Ilfracombe
Devon EX34 8BA

MY NORTH STAR

The end of the second millennium is just forty-five minutes away, and there's not a soul on the promenade. There was going to be a firework display on the pier and entertainments on the prom. But – silence everywhere. I am walking the dogs for the last time before going to bed. The twentieth century is about to pass and the twenty-first to arrive, but the posters all have 'CANCELLED' written across them. The New Millennium is postponed! Lack of interest; shortage of money; everything cancelled.

Barry and I have been together for nearly three decades and our flat on the seafront has only a small patio, so the dogs ensure that we have plenty of exercise: every time they want to cock a leg, it's a walk to the pier. I notice that the lamp posts are all rusting at their bases. Let's hope the council has funds to replace them; otherwise they'll be down on the heads of the promenaders!

The clouds are darting across the sky, occasionally covering the full moon so that one moment we are bathed in silvery light, the next, total darkness. With the darkness, the stars leap into view. The Plough is one I always remember: being a country boy, it's the first constellation you get to know – that and the North Star, twinkling brighter than ever this evening as if it is reminding me of what has gone before. What memories! They seem so distant.

"Be quiet – it's only a rocket," I tell the dogs.

Somebody has let off a solitary firework, which has caused the dogs to start barking. Memories come flooding back: my early life, those far-off days. My North Star. I sit down on a bench at the end of the pier. The clouds have sped past and the sky is once more clear. My star has faded in the silvery light – but the memories are clear. They seem so long ago.

Where is my North Star? I've been waiting for an hour now. The noise from the bar below is getting louder; it must be almost closing time, but Dad never says no to anybody who wants another drink. It could be well past closing time.

This is the sound I suppose Mother heard whilst she was waiting for me to be born. So often I've been told by the Saturday-night drinkers how they waited for the nurse to come downstairs to announce the new arrival. And when she did:

"It's a new landlord – a big, bouncy son." How they stamped and cheered and drank my mother's health!

'Where is it? I am freezing.'

We had no central heating and in the winter we ran from room to room as the only fires burning were in the public bars and the back parlour. As I looked out of the window, my breath froze on the windowpanes, making wonderful patterns; they reminded me of the icing on my mother's Christmas cake. Every year that I could remember there was the same ritual in October – always October. No other month was appropriate, so all the ingredients were brought out of the pantry for the grand mixing, and I always waited to lick both bowl and wooden spoon, and then to be told I would get worms for eating raw flour in the mixture, which did not help my digestive juices flow.

My striped flannelette pyjamas were heavy and coarse on my skin and my thick woollen dressing gown made my neck itch. I thought that the three kings didn't have to wait so long for their star! Why did I keep thinking back to last year and that awful eleven-plus exam? Why didn't I have the brains to get through and go with my first love to the grammar school? How I cried when I found that my friend, David, a tidy, neat, agile boy with a passion for fishing, had passed! For two years I had sat next to him; we did everything together; now he had gone to a different school in his smart new blue blazer with a wonderful gold crest of an imperial eagle on his top pocket, his hair slick with Brylcreem. How beautiful he looked whilst I was left behind to cope on my own in a new class with strangers and no friends! Perhaps I would run away as I did on the second day at school in 1953. The teachers had to search the whole village to find me. I seem to remember hiding in a stable with two very large carthorses. The smell of the horse liniment has stayed with me to this day – a smell that seems to arrive if ever I get anxious or angry. I also retain a few mental snapshots of those first few days at school: the smell of sour milk and pee – there always seemed to be a puddle under one of the girls' chairs, whichever classroom we were in.

My North Star – here she came, over the bridge and down the road. Gosh! It was wobbly! The bags must have been very full and heavy. What was it going to be tonight? Chicken, turkey, beef, sherry trifle? I would just have to wait. I did hope Dad was not around. He did not approve of me getting out of bed to stuff myself with food left over from rich folk; he said it was degrading, and that's a word that had not come into my vocabulary.

"Get back to bed, boy" would be his first words if he saw me.

This was always said in a sharp voice which reminded me of a teacher, Miss Allan. Wearing gold-rimmed pince-nez and a bun, she was even-tempered and seemed placid; but if you upset her, she would wrench up the leg of your short trousers and give you a strong slap on the upper part of your leg where it wouldn't show.

So, I crept down the stairs and into the kitchen before Mother arrived. She had been cooking for Colonel and Mrs Callard since they first arrived from Ireland and bought the manor house in the next village. They were used to lots of servants – children from the estate said that they came from America first and had lots of black servants – "dozens of them".

The Callards had a son and a daughter, whom we never saw or played with as they went to a private boarding school in Ireland. They spoke very nice and posh. Perhaps this was what's known as 'class'. I resolved to try and change my speech and talk what Mum called 'classy'.

There was a big dinner party tonight. Several other ladies from the village were there to help serve and wash up.

Mum should be here any moment. 'Here she comes' – I could see her cycle lamp, my North Star! She pushed her bicycle over the car park and the bags looked full in the moonlight. That was why she was wobbling as she came up the road. I always knew that if my North Star was wobbling there would be lots of goodies on her handlebars – a bag each side to balance the cycle. She always brought all the food that was left over from the parties. Mrs Callard did not eat leftovers!

'She should be so lucky,' I thought to myself.

"Hello, Mum. Saw your lamp coming over the bridge. I could tell there'd be plenty tonight."

"Yes," she replied, "they never seem to eat very much if there's plenty of champagne."

As usual, I got a long speech about the amount of waste and how they should have to manage on what we have to: "Then they would eat it all!"

"That's not a good idea – we'd never get anything then," I laughed.

Dad muttered from the front room, "Goodnight. I'm off to bed. I have locked up."

Never much affection from Dad. He didn't know that I was up and in the kitchen, sorting out the bags.

What was it going to be tonight? I could feel my taste buds swelling and the bubbles of delight around my mouth.

"Mum, what is this pink stuff like wrapping paper? Gosh! It's so good – very smoky."

"That's smoked salmon. They always serve that," she replied.

"And these tiny black balls? They are delicious and very fishy."

"Caviar – fish eggs from Russia. Now be quiet – I've had enough chatter tonight," she finished.

Now I found more small eggs, hard-boiled, this time in jelly, and I knew what they were because I had had them before: quails' eggs in aspic. What a feast!

"No more," she said. "You will be sick. You can have some more tomorrow for your lunch."

"Just tell me what's in these other bags, then I'll go to bed."

"There is some lemon sole, grouse, and crème caramel."

"Goody, goody! Crème caramel – my favourite. What a feast for tomorrow!"

I knew that they were a favourite of the Colonel as Mum often brought them home from the Manor.

This performance went on almost every weekend. My love of food was taking over from my other love, who had gone to the grammar school!

Another birthday, and not a weekend, so no goodies came from the Manor this evening. I would have to wait a few more days for my delights!

"Mum, why couldn't you arrange for my birthday always to fall at the weekend?" I shouted.

"You've got jelly [they always wobbled suggestively; the boys at school called the older girls' breasts 'jellies'], tinned peaches and cake for tea," she replied.

"And bread and butter," I answered back.

Didn't she realise my taste buds had been raised to new horizons. I would never be able to put up with school meals again: overcooked cabbage, tough meat in thin gravy, and stodgy rice pudding with jam that had never seen fruit! So I would have to have sandwiches.

We had such wonderful food arriving at weekends. I could impress my new school chums when they asked, "What have you got in your sandwiches?"

"Smoked salmon, pheasant, grouse, duck and pâté de fois gras!"

"What's that 'grass' stuff?"

Remembering what Mum had told me, I explained: "It's goose liver. They force-feed the geese by stuffing food down their necks, and it makes their livers extra-large, which are made into a pâté."

"Oh, God, we could never eat that," they all replied.

And that put them off asking any more questions about my lunch pack.

Mum even went further by buying something she called Tupperware – small boxes made of plastic from America – and moaned, "These are not to be lost. They cost me a small fortune."

She carefully arranged the leftovers in them: one box for cold pheasant, one for smoked salmon and potato salad, and one for crème caramel.

These lunch boxes were starting to impress and I seemed to be getting more and more new friends. Was it me or my food they were interested in? It had got me worried.

One day Dad actually sat down to tea with us. It was a bit early for opening time and *The Archers* hadn't started on the wireless. Always *The Archers*, then opening time at seven o'clock.

"Now you are thirteen you could earn your pocket money. We need some beaters for the shoot at the weekend," he said.

Although we ran a public house, it did not make enough money to keep us. At least, that's what Dad was always telling me. So Dad worked as a gamekeeper for Lord Janney at Rafflesthorpe and Mum cooked, on special occasions, for Mrs Callard. She had even been known to cook for Lady Janney – but not so often.

"That's how we manage to keep bread on the table," he always reminded me.

He seemed to forget about the rabbits for pies, pigeons for casseroles, pheasant, duck, partridge, snipe, woodcock, waterhen and hares. We seemed to have these very often with our bread and butter! I guess they were excess requirements from Lord Janney's estate, or perhaps Lord Janney didn't know about them. I dared not ask!

I had thought it strange for him to sit down to tea with us; it was to get the word 'work' into my life.

How I had enjoyed the school holidays! They always seemed to be full of sunshine – swimming in the river, camping under the trees, fishing, and frying everything we caught in a large frying pan over a wood fire – pike, perch, tench and even eels, although we had a hard job trying to kill them by hitting them on their heads before getting them in the pan.

Easter holidays were bird-nesting time. Nobody minded in those days. There were hundreds of birds, so a few eggs didn't matter. I had a large collection all kept in old chocolate boxes, wrapped in cotton wool. We never had the chocolates – the boxes came from the Manor. Sometimes there would be one or two left in the bottom layer. I loved the deep Black Magic boxes – black with a red sash of ribbon.

How we loved the flat pastures by the river! There were hundreds of lapwings. Their eggs were so rich and we loved to fry or boil them. They were delicious – so much better than the quails' eggs I got to know later in life. We hoped that they had not been sat on so that there was no blood or baby chick inside. Wonderful summer days! And now work!

God, it was raining so hard and all that walking over sugar-beet fields and woodland to keep Their Lordships happy!

Dad was always at his happiest when organising the guns into their positions. He didn't take any stick from anyone – lords, sirs or just plain honourables. They were all told where to go!

A lot of noise and bustle was coming from the far door and dogs came pouring in as if they were on the scent of a rabbit. They must have got a scent of the pork pies – they probably smelled a bit like their own food because I didn't see them heading for the trestle tables covered with white linen cloths. They all settled at our feet, looking for morsels, then in came the guns. We all kept our heads down, talking to the dogs, but I was watching from the corner of my eye, taking note of what was happening. There was a lot of laughter and a stripping-off of waxed jackets and deerstalkers.

Now glasses were tinkling and they were all settling down to fill their stomachs. Mind you, several of those stomachs seemed monumentally full already!

Who was the person at the bottom of the table? I knew it was Lord Janney at the top end – slight physique, shapely hands with slender fingers and always smelling of bay rum. I didn't know what the smell was until one day I asked my dad after we had met Lord Janney on the estate.

Dad was always surprised when I asked questions about people. He'd just give me a strange look. When I asked about marriage and babies, he would tell me to ask my mother.

She would always say, "Wait awhile – I'll tell you later," and then change the subject.

I never got to know.

The man at the bottom end of the table looked like His Lordship, but very young. So dark, with wonderful shiny black hair, long eyelashes and a warm wide smile, but he was certainly much quieter than the others.

Why was I getting this strange feeling in my stomach? Something was happening. Suddenly I didn't feel very interested in pork pies. Perhaps it was the cider? Strange, strange, strange.

Now he was finishing his meal and looking over to where we were sitting. He got up and headed towards us.

"Hello. My spaniels seem to have settled with you all." Such a deep voice.

Why did I feel this way?

He was looking over at me and saying, "Hello."

I answered, "Hello," not knowing what else to say. Did I feel myself going red?

He asked my name and who I was.

"I'm the gamekeeper's son, Robin," I told him.

He introduced himself as James Janney, Lord Janney's son, and shook my hand. My knees turned to jelly!

Tractors with trailers arrived and we set off to the water meadows for woodcock and duck.

Several times during the afternoon, when the beaters reached the guns, I got a welcome from the spaniels and a smile from James.

The winter was over and the shooting season finished and I had only seen James at one other shoot. No more going to the Hall – I must find some other way to get there.

Easter was here and, believe it or not, there I was asking Dad for work! He told me he had several acres of sugar beet to hoe. He did this in the evenings now that it was lighter and it brought "a bit extra in to put some bread on the table", he explained.

He told me he would teach me what to do and that I could earn about £1 for every twenty rows. He did not tell me that the rows disappeared over the brow of the hill! But who cared? I was off to the Hall Estate and I was in love. Being in love was going to be a painful business!

Several nights passed. My back was bent double with aches

and pains and the five-mile-each-way bike ride didn't help. This must have been love.

On the sixth evening, as the sun was setting and I was just finishing my eighth row, a Land Rover pulled up at the gate and out popped two springer spaniels followed by the Honourable James, as I had been told by Dad to refer to him.

"Just checking the growth of the beet," he said with that wonderful smile. "I didn't know you were helping your father," he continued.

"Yes, I'm trying to earn some pocket money." I couldn't tell him I'd been dying to meet him again. "Dad says it will make a man of me and give me some muscles." What else could I say?

He seemed to be impressed.

"It's hard work. You're a bit young to be doing a man's job."

"No, it's fine." I could feel the colour rising again.

He walked up the field and back, smiled and said, "Goodnight. Keep up the good work." And with that he was gone.

The day was over and I went back home, ten shillings richer and worn out, and I thought I was in love again! The five miles home seemed to fly – I didn't remember pushing the pedals round. I guess it was all worth the effort.

Summer came – and went – with a few sightings of James, and life seemed good. Any job Dad suggested at the Hall, I was more than willing. I think I surprised Dad, and I was building up a small amount of cash. I thought it would be nice to buy a sports jacket like the one I had seen James wearing.

Winter, and back to beating, and James was much more chatty every time I saw him. Another birthday and – wonderful! – it landed on a weekend when Mrs Callard was having a Valentine's party, so I expected to get a good menu for my birthday feast.

Food was taking a hold of my brain, and I was thinking perhaps I would be a chef when I left school.

No 'early to bed' that night! I had some of Mum's records on the wind-up gramophone – Frankie Laine. Dad had let me stay up. He was busy in the bar. Saturday nights were always the busiest. He even told me that if I'd like to come into the bar, he would show me how to pull a few pints and change over the barrels. Busy, busy, busy! Dad showed me how to pour a tot of spirits and how to mix a dry Martini.

I was feeling well pleased with myself in my white shirt and bow tie, when in came a group of people. I couldn't believe it – James was one of the party!

I was trapped behind the bar. Better make this look good. Lots of hellos, to various people, and a loud hello with that smile.

"Hello, Robin. I see your father is keeping you busy this evening. I would like two whiskies, a gin and tonic, and, for myself, a dry Martini."

Dad completely mortified me by saying, "Robin makes a good dry Martini."

"Fine, then he can make me one!" – in a very telling voice.

This had to be good, so with a shaking hand I set to work to make James's drink: one tot of French vermouth; three tots of gin; stir into a tall glass; a dash of orange bitters and a twist of lemon peel over the top and drop into the glass. The love that was going into that cocktail as I passed it to James over the bar!

He smiled and put it to his lips, downed it and, to my delight, ordered another, also adding, "It's the favourite drink of the knowing man."

Another smile.

I would have to find out just what he meant. My birthday was made, and whatever delicacies were brought home later had been slightly eclipsed.

Of course, Dad had to mention that it was my birthday, and I reddened again. They all left in great spirits as they were going to Mrs Callard's for the Valentine's party. I guess it was all glamorous and dizzy entertainment for them – perhaps one day it would be part of my world. I hoped Mum didn't say anything embarrassing or speak to James about me or I would kill her! I didn't wait up at the window that night, waiting for my North Star. Perhaps I would never see her coming over the bridge and up the road again because now that Mrs Callard enjoyed Mum's cooking so much, she was arranging for people to collect and return her in their cars to save her cycling.

Mum was not at home when I was ready for bed, so I guessed there would be no food. Never mind – I'd had my evening in the bar and what more did I need for my birthday than to mix two Martinis for the one I loved? How was it that I'd already forgotten about the one at grammar school with the Brylcreemed hair? I was now into something more romantic.

Sunday morning, only to be told that Mum was driven home in James's Land Rover. The party had gone on so late and Mrs Callard had asked her to stay on to help. Then she was driven home by James and his friends as they were passing on their way home.

Did I need charlotte russe or devils on horseback for breakfast? Cornflakes that morning, I thought, especially after those Martinis last night!

I was just going to the back door when I heard a noise of car wheels on the gravel forecourt – a car? Who could it be that early on a Sunday morning?

The pub didn't open until twelve noon on Sundays and Dad always listened to *Forces Favourites* before he opened the bar.

It was James! He was carrying a bundle of fluff, which was moving and making a noise. Four legs trying to run as the liver-and-white puppy came tearing towards me.

"Happy birthday, Robin. My bitch has had a litter of puppies and I thought you might like one. They are springer spaniels – wonderful gun dogs."

Words were not coming.

"Thank you," I finally managed to stammer.

Mum must have been talking. Only two weeks ago I had mentioned that I would like a dog to train as a gun dog and take with me when I went beating. If I learned to use a gun, it would be useful to have a well-trained dog. She must have told him last night. This was all becoming too much, but was I humiliated? NO!

Another year of beating and sugar-beet hoeing in the holidays. Then summer arrived, and a bonus: Lady Janney asked if I would go and help in the garden. I already knew a bit about gardening because we had gardening lessons at school. I also helped Dad in the garden at home. We had to have lots of vegetables to go with the 'bread', so it was row after row of parsnips, carrots, turnips, cabbages, peas, and beans of every sort. There was always half an acre of potatoes, early and late varieties.

So, I became a gardener.

The summer of 1963 was hot and I sweated away, weeding and cleaning out the greenhouses at the Hall. The greatest pleasure, if James was at home, was when he appeared with cider – always cool and in a large glass. I had to be careful because once before, at a shoot, I had three glasses and I don't think I walked straight all afternoon!

That summer, of '63, I floated on a cloud, but soon summer was over and I went back to school. But there was a bonus in store; Lady Janney asked if I would like to come over on Saturdays to work in the gardens. How the pedals of my bike turned those five miles! I could have flown there on wings of desire!

Most of what I believed I loved and wanted was at the Hall, and not at home.

The gardener was off on Saturdays, so I had the place to myself. I could dream that the garden was mine and that I was strolling, like James, in a straw hat.

Once more back at school and Careers Day was approaching. What was I going to do with my life? Not too much brain: maths, average; English, not too good; history and geography, always near the top in those. Gardening or gamekeeping? Did I have the stamina to work outside in the winter?

Perhaps I was getting too soft. If so, the answer must be – a chef! One more year to go at school, so I would swap woodwork – I was not too good at mortise-and-tenon joints, and I didn't like the woodwork teacher very much. I knew the answer: I would join Miss Bates' cookery class for my last year.

My housemaster soon sorted it out and domestic science was on for Tuesdays and Thursdays in my final year. Mum had to get me a large white apron because I had grown a lot in the past few months.

Now I was taking food home – quiches, pies and casseroles, but I didn't see any smoked salmon or caviar on the school menu. They didn't seem to realise my potential! I would just have to start with the basics and learn the hard way.

Mum told me I could help with the cooking at the Manor for Mrs Callard when there were large parties.

"You can also meet Lydia, her daughter," she said.

"Why would I want to meet her?"

"She is a nice girl."

"I'm too young to have a girlfriend," I replied.

I thought Mum had grand ideas about me meeting and marrying into a higher class. Anyway, I had already been allocated a girlfriend – Mary, who had been asked over on special occasions or at Christmas, since the age of five. She was always asked to go on school trips to the seaside, and had always wanted to hold my hand, but, what with her pigtails and freckles, I was not too keen. I seemed to remember an episode under the dining table, where I was hiding from her. She followed and asked me to show her my willy, and I told her she would have to show me her private parts. That's what she called it! She pulled her knickers aside! What was I meant to see! I suspected she was cheating me and that somewhere there was a lot more. I laughed, but she still wanted to kiss me. But it was not doing anything for me. From that day, at the age of six, I think I knew that I was heading in a different direction.

Both families seemed to have in mind a wedding in about fifteen years' time. Mary's family had a smallholding with a few acres about half a mile down the road – dangerously close! I went through courtship, engagement and marriage before the age of ten. I had been on that planet, but had now moved into a different orbit. Now Mum had me moving up the social ladder to a higher level! I might be, but to a different one altogether from the one she intended.

The appointed evening arrived. I dressed in clean shirt and bow tie.

"You can help serve in the dining room. Mrs Gadesby is helping, so she will tell you what to do."

I turned to go to the front door.

"No, not that way – we use the back door," she said sharply.

"That's not fair," I replied tartly.

Heading towards the back door, I saw a large sign: 'Tradesmen and Servants'. This wasn't on. I didn't think of myself as a servant.

I had been to the fleapit of a cinema in town, cycling all twelve miles to see *Gone with the Wind*, in which the servants are black, large and silent. I certainly didn't fit into that bracket. Something had got to change.

Mum piped up: "If you don't think of yourself as a servant, you can call yourself a tradesman."

"A few steps up, I suppose," I replied, satisfied for the moment.

The evening was going very well. I had checked out the kitchen and Mrs Gadesby had shown me the dining room. So much silver on the table! It glistened like Aladdin's cave. We only had one piece of silver at home. It was a large silver jug with engraving on it. I could never get to look at it properly as it was locked up in Mum's china cabinet and I could not see what was written on it because it was always turned the wrong way round.

Once when I asked Mum why, she replied, "Because I like the other side best." And no more was said.

Mrs Gadesby told me to serve the chicken-liver pâté from the silver platter on to the plates. This was done with a pair of silver tongs.

When I walked into the dining room the guests were already seated at the table. What a relief to see two faces I knew: Lord and Lady Janney! They both spoke to me nicely. Mrs Callard was always a bit stiff when she spoke, but I felt I could easily be sitting at the table with Lord and Lady Janney. I knew all would go well with them there, and it did. At the end of the meal I was a pound richer and there were all the leftovers – not a bad evening.

Another year and another birthday falling on a Sunday. I thought I might be lucky with a few leftovers. Mrs Callard was having a cocktail party. Her guests always seemed to drink more than they ate.

"Mum, why don't you make more food than usual? Then there

will be plenty left over to bring home and fill my Tupperware boxes."

"You are getting too big for your boots. Anyway, you are certainly growing too large."

I had noticed that I had grown, both upwards and outwards. I was already as large as Dad.

My Tupperware boxes were very good because they kept the food from mixing up. Before, it was always put into greaseproof bags and whether or not the turkey and the trifle got mixed together depended on whether or not Mum hit a pothole on the way home, on her bicycle.

The boxes were a bit empty that night – delicacies thin on the ground. A few prawns on top, which I was rather partial to, especially the larger ones; quails' eggs and a little caviar at the bottom.

"I'm afraid all the guests finished off your favourite smoked salmon," she told me.

I'd better be grateful – she had brought home a half-bottle of champagne in her bag. The bubbles were still there. This was good. I'd better make a note of the name: Moet et Chandon. Well, on the whole it was not a bad haul and it had perked up my taste buds. I thought I should be able to brag at school tomorrow that I had caviar and champagne on my fifteenth birthday. I thought that should impress them.

It was just as well that Mrs Callard's children were away in Ireland and did not attend our school. They would soon guess where all this food was coming from.

No work at the Hall until Saturday and I knew that James would not be there as he was taking Lord Janney to London Airport for his flight to America. He was going on business and to visit his sister, who lived in New York.

So, it was a busy day on Saturday. I hoped that it would snow or rain so that I could potter about in the greenhouses. They all needed spraying to kill the bugs before the grapevines started to shoot.

Saturday – wonderful! The snow was falling in large, white, fluffy flakes. Not too good for a cycle ride, so I had better wrap up warmly and make a start. There were a lot of jobs to be done.

Next morning, Sunday, at breakfast I was told to stop chattering. Dad was listening to the news on the wireless. There were a few things he listened to and I had to keep dead quiet. Even Mum kept her lips buttoned. Usually it was only *The Archers*, *Family Favourites* and the news, so it was not that bad.

Dad was looking very serious – something was up. I hoped that I had not done anything wrong, but I would soon know if I had.

"There has been an accident. An aeroplane crashed yesterday whilst taking off from London Airport to New York. It was in a snowstorm and apparently the wings iced up," he said, looking very serious. "It crashed in Surrey, not far from the airport, just after taking off."

"But that is where Lord Janney was flying from yesterday," Mum replied.

Dad was up and out into the hall before anything more could be said, and the next moment we heard him speaking on the phone.

"Who is he speaking to?" I asked Mum.

"I expect to the Hall to see if everything is all right."

"Do you think Lord Janney was on it?"

"I don't know; now be quiet so that I can hear."

From the hall: "Hello. Yes, Mrs Beeston, it's Partner. I have just heard the news on the wireless and I—"

No more was said, so I was unable to follow what was happening. We heard the phone go down and, before we could say anything, Dad walked through the door, tears streaming down his face.

Nothing was said until he was seated in his chair, and after a long silence he told us, "Lord Janney was on that aeroplane and there were no survivors."

Now we all knew the worst, and Mum left the room and walked into the garden. My thoughts were with James. How I wanted to see him!

My tweed jacket had been put on hold. Dad told me that we had to go to the funeral on Friday, so we had to cycle to town to go to Mr Manners, the gents' outfitter. Dad told me I would have to buy a black overcoat. This was not at all what I had in mind for my hard-earned cash. Ever since I had seen James in his sports jacket, that was what my top priority had been. He had always looked so handsome in his. Now it had to be a black overcoat!

Dad bought the first black coat he tried on, but this wasn't for me, so I fussed around and finally Mr Manners brought out a very smart charcoal-grey coat with a velvet collar. This was more like it, particularly as I had seen Lord Janney in a similar one. Not only had my expectations gone up on food, but now they were going up on clothes.

Of course, it cost a lot more and Dad wasn't too pleased. He had no idea about nice clothes.

"Far too much money. Why don't you buy the black one?" he said rather impatiently.

"But, Dad, it is my hard-earned money. Why can't I have what I like?" I remonstrated.

"But you have not earned enough money yet."

"Well, if not, you can lend me some and take it out of my next pay packet."

He scoffed and muttered, "It's your money, if you want to waste it. You pay me back at the end at the month."

He paid for both coats and we left the shop.

So now I was in debt. Not that that mattered. I felt good and looked good; and as James and his family were all going to be there, nothing else mattered – least of all, money.

The day was cold and bright and the roads had a lot of slush on them after so much snow had fallen in the last two weeks, so Dad said, "Put your rubber boots on. We can change them behind the church." He was one for never having anything spoiled. "Too hard-earned," he always said.

We were there early, and with the other estate workers we sat at the back of the church. I had never seen so many flowers: arum lilies by the dozen. Ever since that day they have been one of my favourite flowers – those and lily of the valley. They always came out early at the Hall because the lily beds were so close to the heated greenhouses and Lady Janney liked to have them flowering from February through to October.

The organ struck up and we all stood as they filed in with the rector (a white-haired, well-scrubbed man with pink cheeks) in front. His wife was hardly ever seen and was understood to suffer from some mysterious, and possibly shameful, illness, so it was rumoured in the village. Close behind came the coffin, carried by some of the estate workers. I had wondered why some of the men were missing from the pews. Lady Janney followed the coffin, her arm through James's, her face covered by a black veil – I was instantly reminded of a newspaper picture of the Queen and the two princesses at the funeral of King George. There followed Lord and Lady Woodhouse, the latter rather fussily dressed. Veronica was James's elder sister and, it was rumoured, had married Lord Woodhouse for his money. He was dressed in a very elegant style, but just a little too tight and pompous. I had only met Veronica once – last summer, in the garden. She had come over to have lunch with her mother. I was introduced, but there was hardly a murmur from her. 'Stuck-up' were the words that came to mind. I could see that Lady Janney was none too pleased.

What a lovely person Lady Janney was, and now all this pain and grief! I could feel a tear coming – was it for her or James? I think, for them both.

Then followed Sir Simon Calthorpe, a seemingly kind and gentle man, and his wife, Lady Daphne, the younger of James's sisters, accompanied by their two sons, Angus and Frazer. I judged them to be not much younger than myself. They were obviously of Scottish origin for the boys and their father all wore kilts – something I had not seen in Norfolk before. I remembered that was where Lord and Lady Janney always went to at the beginning of August, for the grouse shooting on the Glorious Twelfth, my dad always said. Thinking back to when I was younger, I remember Dad going with them a couple of times to help to arrange the beaters for the grouse shoots.

Mum used to say that he was going on his holidays to Scotland, and he would retort, "Bloody holidays! I would rather stay at home than try to organise those bloody heathens."

A whole array of people followed the family: men in army and naval uniforms; others in morning suits; ladies in black suits and hats, all veiled so that I could not see if they were weeping. I am sure there were no tears coming from Lady Veronica. I bet she was too busy wondering if she would be getting anything from the will.

A cascade of sound came from the organ; several hymns were sung. There was a lengthy oration from a naval officer, and then we were out once more in the churchyard. The family and close friends had all made their way to the end of the churchyard where the family plot was located.

Dad said, "It's time for us to go home."

"But, Dad, the vicar says everybody is welcome to go back to the Hall for refreshments."

"It's not for us," he said sternly.

"But he said everyone," I replied stubbornly.

"OK, but as I have cycled all this way, I will check my plants and follow you home later."

I hoped he would not press me any harder.

"Yes, all right, but keep out of the way," he said, and he left to pick up his bike.

My plants were a collection of indoor plants which Lady Janney had given me to look after. Some were taken into the Hall and then changed over the following week because some areas inside the Hall did not get much daylight and the leaves on the plants tended to go yellow. So I was in charge of rotating them. I enjoyed this because I could move about the Hall and this gave me more chance of meeting James.

Now I no longer saw him just in his waxed jacket and corduroys, but also in shirtsleeves and, once, even in his dressing gown. It looked like silk – dark maroon with a dragon on the back. I heard that he had been to Hong Kong a couple of years before with his father, on business, so I guessed it was either Chinese or Japanese. Now I had to save, not only for a sports jacket, but also for a silk dressing gown!

Thinking of the dressing gown, I remembered that once when Mum came home from Mrs Callard's she had a bundle of clothes with her. Mrs Callard always gave her the 'cast-offs' – that's what Mum called them. Among them was an ivory silk dressing gown with tropical birds embroidered on it.

"What good is this?" she said. "It's so thin it wouldn't keep a sparrow warm." And then she threw it into the back of the airing cupboard next to the Raeburn oven we had in the kitchen.

I thought I'd better get it out and see how it looked. It would save a few of my hard-earned pounds if it fitted.

Cycling up the drive back to the Hall from the church, I could hear the sound of the crunching of car wheels on the gravel drive behind me. There was nowhere to shelter because I had just passed the last large oak tree – I could have stood behind it.

Dad's strict words came into my head: "Take your hat off."

I had borrowed his best flat cap. He was wearing his Sunday trilby.

So I got off my bike and, standing still, took off my cap. The first car contained Lady Janney and Lord James. I could not keep my head down, so I looked up only to see Lord James give me a smile as they passed. My sadness evaporated a little because of that smile. As the rest of the cars passed me, I looked at the ground. One smile was enough!

As I approached the Hall, I could see all the cars emptying, but I branched off the drive up the grass path to the back of the walled garden, past the bothy and into the greenhouses.

The sun had come out and it was warm inside, so I carefully took off my smart new coat and hung it away from the whitewashed walls. They were fatal, for whenever you touched them you were left with a great white patch. Soon the warmth made me remove my jacket and shirt. It got so tropical inside and I wanted to trim some of the pot plants. There was nothing to go home for, so I thought I might as well stay there.

The smell from the flowers was wonderful. This was the second smell to stay with me along with the horse liniment from when I was younger. I could hear footsteps outside and the greenhouse door opened and James appeared. I had hoped he would come over. I had seen him in the greenhouses a couple of times before and knew there was a chance he would realise that I was to be found there.

He smiled and said, "Thank you for coming to my father's

funeral, and please say thank you to your father for me. My mother also sends her thanks to you both."

I could hardly speak, but I must.

"I am so sorry. Your father was a kind and thoughtful man." I had heard Mum say this to Dad the evening before. I continued: "He will be sadly missed."

Tears welled up in James's eyes and before I had finished speaking he came up to me and put his arms around my body.

After a few moments he said again, "Thank you."

I was so taken aback although I rather thought this was what I had wanted to happen. My mind was racing, but instinct told me to do the same and I put my arms around him.

After a few moments, we parted and he said, "Why don't you come up to the Hall?"

"No, I only wanted to see you to say how sorry I am, and ask you to say the same to Lady Janney," I said, wiping my own tears away.

We stood there awhile, looking at the flowers and breathing in their scent.

"I'd better get back. How is Bella? Have you got her trained yet? Oh! I'm sorry that I forgot your birthday – so much has happened." And, with that, he was gone.

Next morning, Saturday again.

"You are not going over to the Hall this morning?" said Dad.

"Yes, there is a lot to be done and I need to earn some pocket money to pay for that coat I will never wear again."

"You will have lots of occasions to wear it; and if you look after it, it will last a long time. That's why I told you to buy the larger one."

Why is it, when you do not have much money, you always have to buy clothes too large? Most of my school clothes had always been too large, with cuffs that covered my hands. I always remember going to school on Commonwealth Day – it was an occasion to look forward to. The school was hung with flags and we had a special lunch. At the climax of the celebrations all the children marched round the hall singing 'Land of Hope and Glory' and waving Union Jacks. But my shoes were too loose and my trousers and jacket too large. I felt I wanted to run and hide; I must have been fashion-conscious even at that early age.

"But you don't need to go in today. Lord James has given everybody the weekend off – except the cowmen, as milking has to go on whatever happens."

"Even if an atomic bomb lands on this country the cows will still have to be milked," I replied. "Remind me not to be a cowman. There is nothing else to do as it's raining, so I will go up to the greenhouses. Anyway, Lady Janney asked me if I would clean out the fruit store," I added, desperately searching for anything that would take me up to the Hall.

"Keep away from the house as all the family are staying for the weekend. They have plenty on their plates for a while."

"Yes, Dad. I'm off now."

Even when it was wet, the greenhouses were always warm. The fruit store was joined to the back of the greenhouses. The bottles that held the grapes when they were cut needed to be washed with disinfectant. That gave me an excuse to go to the Hall kitchen and ask the cook for some hot water.

"Come in – it's freezing out there," the cook said as I knocked on the door and entered.

"Please can I have some hot water? I am washing the grape bottles out."

"Hang on a minute and I'll fill your pail."

"Where is everybody? It's so quiet."

"I think they are still eating their breakfasts. Nobody got up very early this morning after the funeral yesterday."

"Yes, it was so sad."

"Lord James will have to take charge of everything now he has inherited the estate," she replied.

I had not even thought of him having all the estate.

"Here you are, and keep in the warm. Your father will not be too pleased if you get a cold."

"Thank you," I said, and I was off, back to the garden.

As I walked back to the greenhouses, I was met on the path by the two boys.

"Hello. I'm Angus and this is my brother, Frazer. Who are you? We saw you in church yesterday."

"I'm Robin. I help in the greenhouses and my father is the gamekeeper," I told them.

"What have you got that water for?"

"I'm going to wash the grape bottles."

"What are they?"

"They are the bottles that we put the ripe grapes in when we have cut them. The stalks are put in the bottles, which are filled with water, and it keeps them fresh for the kitchen."

"Wow! Can we come and help?"

When we were back in the greenhouse, I soon set them the task of washing the bottles. Perhaps I had got some of Dad's organising skills – especially with the landed gentry!

Trousers soaking wet, they had soon finished the job.

"Robin, we have done them all and I think we had better get back to the house. Mother will start to worry where we have got to."

"Thank you. That's been a great help."

"We will see you when we come to stay in our school holidays. Cheerio." And they were gone.

With that job out of the way, I made my way into the apple store and removed all the hay off the shelves where the apples had been stored. The store was not very light, as the apples had to be kept in the dark. I switched on the light, but the bulb was covered in dust. Just as I was transferring the last of the apples on to some new hay, I heard footsteps coming through the greenhouse.

"Hello, Robin."

"Good morning, sir," I said, rather too fast.

"Sir? I want you to call me James."

"But my parents have told me to call you sir."

"That may be so – you can when there are other people around, but when we are by ourselves you can call me James."

I was not too sure about this, but, as he had told me himself, it would be my secret.

"Yes, OK, James," I replied, blushing slightly.

"I missed your birthday, and as I have inherited all my father's guns I thought you might like to have this one. I had it when I was about your age."

All I could muster was a quiet "Thank you" as I handled the gun.

"It is a 4.10 which folds in half so you can hide it under your coat or in your boots."

"Why?"

"Because it's a poacher's gun. Your father knows all about them!"

"It's amazing," I said as the cartridges were handed over to me.

First a gun dog, now a gun! Perhaps I should have been a gamekeeper rather than a chef.

He was so close.

All I could say was "Thank you" again, and I put my hand out to shake his – another of Dad's lessons.

Instead of taking my hand, he did the most unexpected thing. Quickly, before I was aware of what was happening, he put his arms around me and kissed me on the lips. My mouth opened in surprise and I felt, for a brief second, his tongue against mine. Another second and he had gone. I suddenly realised that, not only did I like the kiss, I was eager to experience it again.

What was I to do or say the next time we met? And, riding home, I wondered how to explain why Lord James had given me one of his guns for my birthday.

"Hello, Dad. Look what Lord James has given me. He says that if I can learn to shoot, as well as train Bella as a gun dog, I can train as an under-keeper when I leave school."

This is what I'd been planning to say on the way home, and it seemed to be going down fairly well.

"But I thought you were going to be a chef."

"Well, if I've got two options I can choose when I leave school."

"Up to you – your business," Dad said rather briskly.

That was sorted out. One thing about Dad: he never asked too many questions and was always satisfied with a simple answer.

Mum was totally different: she wanted to know the ins and outs of a duck's arse, as I once heard one of the beaters say! It is amazing what you pick up from your elders when you are young – not that I'd ever dare repeat it in Mum's hearing!

That night, I lay in bed trying to relive what had happened in the apple store – the fullness of his lips and his black hair. I closed my eyes and tried to recreate the sensation.

School again, but I felt so grown-up. Those last few months, before I left at Easter, I knew were going to be very hard. The cookery had gone very well and I had a place at the City Technical College for a two-year course aimed at getting City and Guilds Certificates 147 and 150. This meant that the gamekeeper in me must be put to one side.

One night, at the Manor, Mrs Callard was giving a special party for her daughter, who was back from school in Ireland. Being at school, she had missed her seventeenth birthday. A band had been booked and there was to be a large buffet. Mum had been busy for two days and, as I was at school, she kept me well informed about everything she was making: whole salmon in aspic; chicken cooked and covered in cream sauce and decorated with red and green peppers cut into flowers and leaves; a whole turkey; glazed hams with apricots; chocolate mousse; roulades and trifles. This was too good to miss!

Friday night arrived at last. Mum had been at the Manor all day and I had been told to be ready at six thirty as I was to be picked up by car, dressed in a pressed white shirt, black bow tie, and shoes that you could see your face in – another of Dad's rules.

Dad shouted, "There's a car arriving in the yard."

It was too early for opening time, so I knew it must be my lift to the Manor.

"Yes, I'm coming."

And as I grabbed my coat with the velvet collar, he smiled and said, "I told you a coat would be very useful to have!"

Before there was a knock on the door, I was out in the yard, and there was a gleaming red MG sports car. Oh, God! It was James – this was too good to be true!

"I'm your chauffeur tonight. I hope you don't mind, but I knew you were coming, so I told Mrs Callard that I would pick you up as I was passing your door," he shouted.

As I got in, I said, "Thank you," and was thankful that Dad hadn't put on the outside light because I could feel the colour rising – embarrassment, or was it something else?

One mile in an MG would only take two minutes to the Manor. Why didn't Mrs Callard live 100 miles away? A touch of hands instead of a handshake – no room for an embrace in a sports car!

At the Manor, cars were drawing up to the front of the house. We sailed straight through the front gates and up to the front door. No back door, servants' or tradesmen's entrance that night! I would walk in with James and keep my fingers crossed that Mrs Callard's butler would keep his mouth shut. I had more courage now that I was with Lord James Janney! If he said anything, I would tell him that I was a friend of Lord James and I thought that would keep him muffled.

Not a word as we went in. The chandeliers sparkled; I smelled the flowers, saw the pictures, felt the warmth. Here I was in at the front door!

As I turned towards the dining room, I said, "Thank you for bringing me. It saved the bike ride."

"Let me know when you are ready to go home and I'll take you," he said, smiling, and walked off towards the reception room.

The party was a great success. Mum had turned out a wonderful spread and everyone was smiling and laughing, eating and dancing. Several times I saw James dancing with Mrs Callard's daughter. Was I jealous?

I continued serving the champagne – I thought I'd better try some to see if it was cold enough. Perhaps I should have tried every bottle.

It was just as noisy in the kitchen. There were various women from the village in their black dresses, white pinafores and starched white caps perched on the fronts of their heads. They looked like a flock of penguins, but were as noisy as crows.

The main topic of conversation was Mrs Callard's daughter, who had apparently got her eye on the handsome – no, beautiful – Lord James. This was not on the books. I could see Mrs Callard's plan – hoping to make it up the social ladder so that she would have a daughter whom everyone had to call 'Your Ladyship'. My mind was racing.

As midnight was fast approaching, the next time I filled James's glass it was with champagne. He was currently drinking orange juice, as were several of the other younger members of the party. I wondered if James knew what was going on. Surely he must have cottoned on to what Mrs Callard was up to. He would need a clear head! Isn't it strange how mothers try to organise their children's futures? First, Mum had me down to marry Mary, then her thoughts went to Mrs Callard's daughter and the Manor, and now here was Mrs Callard up to the same tricks. Mum had no idea that my own thoughts had moved on to embrace Lord James and the Hall! That would have really shocked her.

As the party was breaking up, most of the glasses had been cleared. Mum had cleared up an hour ago and one of the village ladies had taken her home. Mrs Callard's butler, who had been very kind to me all evening, had told me not to bother with the few glasses that were left as he would see to them so I would not keep Lord James waiting. It is amazing how kind people are when you move in the right circle of people.

One mile from home and James was driving very slowly. Was it alcohol or did he want to make it longer?

"You must be very tired, what with a day at school and a very busy evening."

"Not really. I have enjoyed it all and been paid £5." I smiled.

Now we were at the bridge over which I used to watch my North Star appearing and bringing all the exciting food. James pulled into the gateway of Colonel Callard's water meadows and my heart was racing madly. Would it happen again?

"Robin, now that my mother is on her own and has reduced the number of staff in the Hall, she wonders if you would like to help at the weekends and during holidays. She thinks you might like to do some cooking as you are training to be a chef."

"I'd love to. It would be good experience."

"She has told the cook she can have the weekends off if we are not entertaining or when there are no guests in the house. There are only the two of us when I'm at home."

This was all too good to be true. Now I would be inside the Hall all the time.

"As you have to cycle five miles every time you come there, you can come over on Friday nights and stay till Monday morning. We have several bedrooms not in use in the wings, so there is plenty of space. You can keep your clothes there for helping in the dining room if we entertain," he said, smiling.

Now I was moving in! Things were moving too fast. I told myself to keep steady.

Smiling, he said, "I would like it as well if you stay. We could play billiards when you are free. I really haven't played since father died."

"I'm not sure I play very well, but you can teach me," I replied, thinking that he had already taught me a few things.

What next? From the intensity of his expression to the holding of hands and the kiss on the lips, it all happened. Momentous things were happening in my life. Like a volcanic eruption.

Car lights were coming up in the distance behind us, so he started the car and we arrived in our yard a few seconds later. I knew this was love.

"Goodnight, Robin. I will see you tomorrow." And he was gone.

Thank God Mum and Dad had gone to bed! No explanations for being too late – just straight to bed with the most wonderful feeling I had ever had.

Three weeks to Christmas. I must get the Christmas plants ready for the Hall. They all needed to be potted up, ready to go into the Chelsea jardinières. How quickly I was learning about good things!

Next day I could hear the clock striking ten from the coach-house roof when into the greenhouse walked Lady Janney with a mug of coffee. Gosh, this was good.

"Good morning, Robin."

"Good morning, Lady Janney."

"James has told me you would like to come and help in the Hall. If you can help at the weekends, we can arrange menus and you can practise on us what you have learned at school. Perhaps you can start next Saturday – we are not having anybody to stay until Christmas, so the cook will not be coming in at weekends."

"That will be fine. I will cycle over next Friday after school and stay over until Monday morning. Lord James told me I could use a spare bedroom."

"That would be very nice," she said as she left me to my thoughts.

So I had two weekends to try out before they had anybody to stay. I was finding this all very exciting.

Mum had got her feet up when I got home and I was bursting with all the news. I told her everything Lady Janney has said and she seemed pleased, but I was not quite sure. Perhaps it was because I would no longer be able to help her at the Callards'.

I was going up in the world, I thought to myself, but Mum soon brought me back to earth with a lesson on 'minding my Ps and Qs'. I'm never really quite sure what that means, but they had been mentioned at very regular intervals those past few years. She wanted to know, when I spoke to Lady Janney, how I addressed her. Did I call her Your Ladyship? I told her that I'd been told to call her Lady Ruth.

"And what do you call Lord James?"

"James," I said.

"You must not call him by his Christian name."

"But that is what he asked me to call him."

"You must call him sir."

"He asked me to call him James, so that is what I am going to call him."

Looking at her with a cold frown, I was feeling angry but determined to stand my ground. I was nearly sixteen and it was time to stick up for myself. Some of my friends at sixteen were earning a wage packet. I could see she was not too pleased, but no more was said.

The next weekend seemed never to arrive. Lady Janney, now to be known as Lady Ruth, had arranged for somebody from the estate to collect me and bring over everything I might need in my room at the Hall. 'My room at the Hall' – I liked the sound of that, but I decided to keep it to myself. How I used to like to brag to my school friends about all the food and things – not any more. This move had to be kept to myself. I must never let it be known that I considered Lady Ruth a friend and that I loved her son, James. It could never be spoken of. We had been reading Oscar Wilde's poetry at school and there had been too much sniggering in the classroom. My new relationship was definitely something not to be mentioned.

On Saturday morning Mr Biggs, the shepherd, arrived with his battered Land Rover full of sheep dogs to collect me. It was a good job I put my clothes in plastic bags, what with the amount of dogs' hairs and mud flying around. But one word from him and all the dogs were sitting in the back with not a hair on their bodies moving. Now, that's what I call training. Bella was getting there steadily. She was still a bit bouncy, but she would soon get out of it and would surely make a good gun dog.

We arrived at the Hall to find a huge yellow Bentley parked outside the front door.

"That's Lord and Lady Muck's Bentley," said Mr Biggs.

"Who's Lord and Lady Muck?"

"That's Lady Veronica – Lady Janney's daughter."

"Oh! I've met her. I'm not over keen."

"I should say not."

He dropped me at the entrance and drove off before anything further could be said and before I could say thank you.

The door was wide open. I wandered up the front steps and, as there was nobody about, I knocked and stepped into the entrance hall. How I loved this house! I felt as if I had arrived home.

"The staff entrance is at the back." I heard a voice coming from the staircase, and looking up I saw Lady Veronica coming down the stairs.

"Good morning, Lady Woodhouse." I had to mind my Ps and Qs even if I didn't like the person. "I have come this way because Lady Ruth—"

"Lady Ruth! It's Her Ladyship to you."

Now, should I keep to my Ps and Qs or should I tell her what Lady Ruth told me?

"Good morning, Robin. Glad to see Mr Biggs has delivered you safely. I'll show you to your room."

It was Lady Ruth and I had been saved by the bell.

"Mother, what is going on?"

"No need for you to worry, Veronica," said Lady Ruth, showing me up the staircase. "I'll tell you later." The tone was final and Lady Veronica stomped off angrily down the corridor.

"I have had Mrs Jordan give the room a good clean as it has not been used for some time. We used to entertain a lot, but those days are gone."

"Thank you, Lady Ruth," I replied.

'Thank you' are words that are worth a lot, especially if you deliver them with warmth and a smile. They get you a long way, and always out of trouble.

The room was pure *Gone with the Wind*: the furniture, the four-poster bed, the china, the curtains, the view from the windows overlooking the park, the connecting bathroom and huge bath, on four giant claws, standing in the middle of the room. All pure magic!

"I'll drown in that," I said, smiling at Lady Ruth.

The towels were so thick I couldn't wait to wrap myself up in one and stay there forever.

"Thank you again."

She smiled and said, "Don't worry about lunch. Just go down to the kitchen after one thirty. Lady Veronica is going to prepare some lunch for me, and she will be leaving afterwards. When she's gone, come and find me in the sitting room. I didn't know she was coming and she is angry that I have told the cook not to come in at the weekends. So she is making lunch because she didn't think you would be much use! We'll show her! Bye."

And with that she was gone.

Oh, how I was beginning to hate Lady Veronica! Hate was not a thing that had really entered my life up to now – except for the eleven-plus exam. But that had dimmed now that I had a new love.

The best thing for me to do was drop down the back stairs – I had made up my mind to call them this as I hated calling them servants' stairs – then out of the back door and over to my beloved greenhouses. How I loved working in them with the scents, and the warmth from the peaches, apricots and figs. Perhaps I was born to live in the Garden of Eden, but I'm not sure how God would have coped with two Adams!

At the sound of the stable clock striking two, I knew I was safe to sneak back to the kitchen. No, I would not 'sneak' anywhere – especially in my own house, for that was what it now seemed to be. I had to have my wits about me and be ready for Lady Veronica at all times. I had seen how Lady Ruth dealt with her. I had to do the same. James would be on my side.

I even got that impression from Lady Ruth when she said, "James will be home at four." She knew it would please me.

No, I would not sneak into the kitchen. I would stroll boldly down the corridor from the back door and hope that she wasn't there. Not a soul. Plenty of dirty plates stacked on the draining board – it looked as if they had had sandwiches. That was not much for Lady Ruth. I was sure her daughter could have done better than that. Perhaps she herself had never cooked and had her own cook. I wouldn't want to be in her cook's shoes!

There were racks of eggs. I thought an omelette would be nice and easy, and there was plenty of salad in the refrigerator. I knew that James was a great fan of salad and fruit from the times he used to come into the garden in the previous summer, or did he just say that so that he could keep coming simply to talk?

I had never seen such large eggs – I realised they must be goose eggs. Four would be enough, mixed well with cream. With a nice mixed salad I thought that would do very well. Now for the dressing – honey, olive oil, mustard and wine vinegar – and in two minutes it was done. My training was coming in handy. With the eggs in the pan, I realised I had not thought about a filling. Then I remembered seeing some smoked salmon in the fridge. A quick chop and this went in with the eggs. By this time, and with the aroma from the pan, I was beginning to feel very hungry indeed. The omelette was looking very large – perhaps I should have used only two eggs.

"I've caught you in the act," said James, arriving in the kitchen soaking wet. "I've been shooting, but it got so bad, and the rain so heavy, we had to finish early. My God! That smells good."

"Goody, because I've made far too much. Never used goose eggs before. I seem to have made enough for six people. Your mother could have had some. Your sister only made a sandwich for her."

"Yes, I saw her car at the front of the house, which is why I came in through the kitchen."

So I had thought correctly – James was not too fond of his sister.

By the time he had climbed out of his boots and waxed jacket, I had two plates of omelette and salad ready. Mrs Beeston, the cook, had a large pine table in the middle of the kitchen. I guessed this was where they all sat when they had finished serving in the main dining room.

James said, "This is nice. I like it. I am so glad you have come to help Mother, and I know she likes you very much."

I really couldn't find an answer. Still only fifteen, and getting into older company, I was not sure how to reply sometimes. As it was, I just smiled and said, "Thank you."

James told me that he was twenty-two, so he was not much older, but he had been to boarding school and university and this made him seem much older than me.

"Eating with the servants?" Lady Veronica said with angry sarcasm as she came into the kitchen with the coffee cups.

I'll bet she was expecting somebody else to wash them up and, as there was nobody else there except me, if she didn't do them, it would have to have been her mother.

I could sense James's unease, but his eyes were averted. However, he was aware of my despair and said, "Robin is no servant. He is my friend, and Mother has asked him if he would like to help us at the weekends."

"Yes, I know. She has told me everything and I have told her she was stupid to stop cook from coming in."

This was my time to make a mark if I was going to hold my own in this house. With a heaviness building in the pit of my stomach, I said, "Lady Veronica, if I had known you could only make a sandwich for your mother, I would have come in from the greenhouses and made you both a smoked-salmon omelette and salad."

James said, "Yes, it's delicious," and carried on eating.

I could see that she was fuming, and as she left the kitchen I wondered if I had overstepped the mark.

Instinctively I knew that I had not when James put his hand on mine and said, "That was splendid of you to put her in her place, but I'm afraid you have made an enemy now."

When we had finished eating, James took me on a tour of the house. I knew most of it from changing the pot plants, but there were various rooms I had not previously seen. Now I had the whole layout of the house in my head.

There were several more bedrooms in the wing where mine was situated, and in the area where the ballroom had been, a swimming pool had been constructed. After the war, in which Lord Janney was wounded, swimming was recommended to help his recovery. Certainly, the days of having balls were long gone, so the floor was dug out and a long swimming pool with four lanes had been put in. This was splendid because James said, "You can use it whenever you like because Mother never uses it and I only swim first thing every morning."

"Wonderful! I can join you in the mornings. We used to swim in the river every summer down by the water meadows."

"Near the bridge?"

"Yes."

"I watched a group of boys swimming during the last few summers. I expect you were one of them."

"You should have joined us," I replied, laughing.

The supper was going to be a simple meal because, after he

had taken me round the house, James suggested afternoon tea, so I prepared some tea and cakes, which I took to the drawing room. When I entered, Lady Ruth was lying on the settee with her feet up.

"Veronica is exhausting. It's a good job she doesn't come too often. After I lost Cameron, I was worried she would want to move in or try to persuade me to go and live with her." I smiled as she continued: "That would have been impossible."

I poured her a cup of tea and she said, "Stay and have one yourself. James will be here soon, so you can pour his too."

As they were both talking, I sat by the window looking out on to the parkland and it occurred to me that I had heard people saying that now James had inherited his father's title and death duties had been paid, money was rather tight and the farms were not bringing in much money. With the costs involved in keeping up the house, and with only the two of them living there, I could quite understand why Lady Ruth had reduced the cook's hours. The maid had left after Lord Janney's funeral, which left only the cleaner, Mr Biggs and the gardener. Mr Landamore, the butler-cum-valet to Lord James, had reached the age of sixty-seven and wanted to retire. His daughter, who lived in the next village, wanted him to go and live with her. He had told Lady Ruth that he was quite willing to come in to help from time to time, when she had house guests. As far as the house was concerned, this left the cook and the cleaner working Mondays to Fridays with me at the weekends and during the college holidays.

When their conversation came to an end, I asked Lady Ruth if she would like a spinach soufflé and salad.

"That will be grand," she said, "and perhaps just a little cheese and fruit to follow."

"I will set up the dining room for you both."

"Robin, make that three settings."

"Of course. Who will be joining you?"

"You, of course. There is no need to take your meals in the kitchen. You can eat with us."

I saw a smile on James's face and a feeling of well-being flooded into my stomach.

"Thank you. That would be very nice" was my reply.

Was this James's doing, or was Lady Ruth aware of what was happening between James and me?

The weekend was soon over. It didn't seem like work: living in a beautiful house with wonderful people and getting paid into the bargain. School was suddenly becoming boring – not too long to go before I finished, and the weekend would soon be here again. My life was measured in weekends. The routine was soon established: Friday afternoon, after school, on my bike for the five-mile ride to the Hall. I preferred to go on Friday because it meant that I was settled in and ready to start work on Saturday morning. It also meant another night at the Hall. Those nights were becoming precious to me. James had already told me that Lady Ruth had her breakfast at nine o'clock. They always used to breakfast in the dining room, but since the loss of Lord Janney she had had it in her bedroom.

Lady Ruth's bedroom was magnificent. Its two floor-to-ceiling sash windows enabled her to look out from her four-poster bed over the parkland landscaped by Humphrey Repton. I had seen a Red Book on the designs of the different landscapes lying on the table in the library. The bed was superb: made in the Regency period, it still had its original hangings. These included wig pouches, which were fixed to the headboard. These fascinated me – it seems so strange to take off one's wig and tuck it into the pouch before getting into bed. The rest of the furniture was wonderful too – Georgian and of the finest mahogany. Each wall was hung with Norwich-school paintings, and each surface boasted perfect porcelain. The flowers, gathered from the gardens, set off the whole effect. The sun radiated through the windows in the early morning so that I could see why she was never anxious to leave it.

James had brought in a card table from the library and two Hepplewhite chairs, and it was here that breakfast was laid out with damask cloth, silver cutlery and a vase of flowers from the garden – much more preferable than the dining room. James always joined her if he was at home and not too busy on the estate.

If farm business meant he had to be away early, he would join me in the kitchen for breakfast at the large table.

On Saturday morning, James came into the kitchen early. I couldn't take my eyes from his face: those wonderful eyes, full lips and black hair were stunning.

As I looked at him he said, "Robin, you know I love you and will always be loyal to you."

I was about to reply when the dogs came charging into the room. Mr Biggs was at the door, wanting to talk to James about one of the breeding ewes.

"See you at lunchtime. I shall be expecting something special," he said as he got up to get his coat.

"Egg and chips" was my reply, and he was gone.

When I took Lady Ruth's breakfast up to her room, she said, "Robin, stay a moment. We can organise the meals for the weekend. Something light for lunch?"

"Omelette, perhaps?"

"Yes, that's splendid, and some salad. For supper, something fishy. Tomorrow we could have a roast. There's plenty of beef in the freezer – we had a whole side frozen when we last sent some for slaughter. I'll leave it to you."

"Fine – I'll sort it out. Just leave it to me," I said as I prepared to leave the room.

"By the way, Robin, I will be away next weekend. James is having some of his chums from university and London to stay and intends to give a dinner party on Saturday evening. No doubt he will mention it to you this evening. Do you think you can manage, or shall I get cook to come in?"

"No, don't worry cook. I can manage – no problem. I will check with James what he wishes to be served and find out how many are coming."

"They are all men," she said.

"Well, there is plenty of game about. That should do the job."

"Thank you. You are so good," she said as I left the room.

The coming weekend had been arranged, and James had told me what he wanted to be served.

The week had passed in a flash and here I was, once again cycling back to the Hall, full of anticipation. At intervals throughout Saturday morning cars and motorcycles arrived and James brought some of his friends through to the kitchen for coffee. I had laid on a buffet lunch in the dining room so that they could help themselves throughout the day. That meant that I could get on with supper. They seemed to be a nice bunch of young men – all very well mannered.

The evening arrived and I went up to bath and dress. I had finished all the preparation and the meal was in the Aga. I changed into my new white shirt and black bow tie. As I passed James's bedroom I noticed that he had already gone downstairs and I could see a large bottle of cologne on his dressing table. I slipped in and tipped a large splash of it into my hands and then on to my face. For one moment, I thought I would lift off – I had not realised how much it would sting – but it made me feel good. As I went downstairs, I was enveloped in a cloud of cologne and began to wonder if I had put on too much.

James's guests were gathering in the library and I served them champagne. They were all rather handsome and dressed in evening dress. I was thinking that it was some kind of celebration that I didn't know of; certainly it was not James's birthday. After I had served them a couple more glasses of champagne, I left them to help themselves and went through to the dining room. I had raided the garden and arranged a large table centre using the last of the white roses and arum lilies. They would just about see each other over them!

When I sounded the dinner gong, they all came cheerily through to the dining room, having consumed a good deal of champers. I thought I got one or two meaningful looks as they passed me on their way to the table. The menu was easy and I had placed the wine on the table for them to help themselves. They started with smoked-salmon pâté – always one of James's favourites – and Melba toast, which was easy to serve. I followed that with pheasant casserole with a selection of vegetables, which, again, they could help themselves to.

I served the pheasant from the wonderful Sheraton sideboard, and as I put the seventh place down a voice said, "James, I think you are paying your waiter too much. He seems to be able to afford the same cologne as you, and we all know what expensive tastes you've got."

There was loud laughter from them all and James replied, "Robin certainly has good taste – one or two of you could take a lesson from him."

More laughter.

I managed to get the rest of the plates to the table without actually dropping anything in my embarrassment.

A rather snooty, blond young man said, "I think James has been too close to Robin." He was smiling as he said it.

I had noticed that one or two of them had been watching me rather too closely, and as I left the room I heard the dark one next to James say, "You've got a pretty one there, James."

Thank God I was out of the room and needn't go back for a good twenty minutes to clear the plates away.

The sweet was a frozen bombe concoction, which I sliced and served with a fruit coulis. I had planned to serve the blond snooty one last to see if I could drop it in his lap. I made sure I had some spare so that at least he wouldn't have to go without. I approached him and, as I got close, pretended to slip and the bombe slid gracefully off the plate and into his lap.

There was great applause and the boy sitting next to him said, "I told you he wouldn't like to be talked about!"

After helping him to clear the mess from his lap, I said, "I do have some more if you still fancy some."

He nodded and said, "Yes, please."

"James," I said as I was leaving the dining room, "I will put the coffee in the drawing room for you so that you can help yourselves after you've had your cheese."

"Thank you, Robin, for a fine meal," he replied.

"And thanks for the entertainment!" they all chipped in, with much merriment.

James came into the kitchen as I was sorting the dishes out.

"Robin, I think it's best if you sleep in my room tonight. I think one or two of my friends are preparing to check you out."

"OK, I'll go straight up when I've finished here," I said.

"See you later." And he was gone.

After clearing up the kitchen, I went up to James's room; although I concentrated hard on keeping awake until he came upstairs, a hard day's work had taken its toll and before he arrived I had drifted into a deep sleep – so deep, in fact, that whatever time he eventually retired he did not disturb me. I suspect that the alcohol had done for James what tiredness had done to me, for when I awoke next morning he was still snoring gently and I hadn't the heart to wake him.

Breakfast that morning wasn't served until eleven o'clock. The guests were somewhat subdued, although I received a few comments, such as "Where did you sleep last night?"

It was clear that some of them had checked my room and most of the others. Several congratulated James for having a sporty friend, and I could tell from the sly looks I was getting that a few had guessed where I had been.

I did offer to pay to have Snooty's trousers cleaned, but he took it all in good part and said, "No problem, and the best of luck with James!"

Events had surpassed all my expectations. What did the future hold for us? At best I knew from conversations I had overheard at school that it would be an illicit relationship. James was kind, gentle and very handsome. He had an adoring mother, who thought the world of him. He was her prized possession and her ever watchful eyes would soon pick up on a competitor for his affections. I did not want to be exiled so soon from the world I had come to know and love. Even if Lady Ruth was prepared to be tolerant, I could not depend on other members of the family being sympathetic.

Christmas was fast approaching and I knew that Cook would be on duty. I made sure that I would be there to help, but said nothing to annoy her or get in her way. I did what she asked of me, and when there was nothing particular for me to do I retreated to my beloved greenhouses.

James had already ushered me out of the kitchen several times to teach me to play billiards, but there was no possibility of this happening with all the family there. This was the first Christmas without Lord Cameron, so all the arrangements would be in James's hands. Now James was master, he would no doubt sit at the head of the table; I was looking forward to seeing Lady Veronica's face!

James had made it clear to me by this time that he considered what Lady Veronica had said to me in the kitchen was an insult and that he would not forgive her; but he also wished things to remain calm during the Christmas period for Lady Ruth's sake.

Of course Cook asked me to help serve Christmas lunch, and I knew that this would be the most difficult period. I knew that, if necessary, I could handle conflict, but hoped there would be none. Above all, I would be able to throw off the constraints of my upbringing and move in another world.

With confidence in James's love, I was beginning to think it possible.

Almost before I knew what was happening, Christmas was here. The family members had all arrived independently and Cook had prepared a buffet lunch. This suited Lady Ruth because the lack of formality meant fewer problems from all the family sitting down together.

Angus and Frazer came to find me in the greenhouses. They seemed to like me and wanted to be friends. Certainly Sir Simon and Lady Daphne didn't seem to mind, as there were smiles all round. I am sure that they had heard Lady Ruth say how helpful I had been and were grateful that their mother was happy with the situation. I could tell from Lady Veronica's face that she did not think it at all appropriate for her nephews to be associating with the gamekeeper's son.

Christmas went smoothly and very quietly. It was the first since Lord Janney's death, so no guests had been invited to stay. James, his nephews and Sir Simon spent most of their time in the billiard room, but the boys also spent a lot of time in the swimming pool and asked me several times to join them when I had finished helping Cook.

Boxing Day was perfect: the family had decided not to join the hunt, out of respect for Lord Janney, but they had gone out to see the huntsmen leave from the front of the Hall – an age-old tradition. Angus, Frazer and I had planned to swim, and, to my surprise, James donned his costume and joined us. Being four, we could have two teams for water polo with the boys on one side and James and I on the other. We had the most perfect hour of fun and one I shall never forget.

With Christmas over, and Lady Ruth a little overtired, peace and quiet once again descended on the house and gardens. I had been kept very busy and had managed to keep well out of the way of Lady Veronica, so no problems had arisen. James had returned to the management of the farms and parkland and Lady Ruth to her old routine of reading and resting. She had dropped most of her charity work and her various committees since the death of her husband. The realisation that things had changed forever had finally caught up with her and she was looking tired and older.

My three weeks at the Hall during the Christmas holidays had come to an end and school was starting on Tuesday.

The last school term before college dragged on forever, but my cookery classes had progressed so well that I was quite sure that becoming a chef was the right course for me. Gamekeeping could be put to one side. Dad didn't seem to mind – at least, he never said a word and he certainly never let anything show on his face. This didn't worry me too much because I had become a good shot and had trained Bella to be a good gun dog. I could now enjoy a day out shooting with James over the estate. I laughed at Dad one evening and said he was to be sure to produce plenty of game for shooting. He looked up, but I simply couldn't read anything into his look. Then he was behind his daily paper again.

James had taken me out on a few occasions over the Christmas holidays and I had bagged a few pheasants and pigeons. Our relationship had developed into an understanding that we loved each other. On a few occasions, he had joined me in my bedroom, in the wing of the Hall, when Lady Ruth had retired to bed. The pattern seemed to be perfectly normal – but what was the future to hold?

February, and another birthday. Sixteen! I had moved on a

long way from the days when I had waited for my wobbly North Star to come up the road from the Manor.

James told me he was going to Venice for a few days and asked if I would like to go with him. My heart raced as I wondered how I was going to tell the family. In the end, I just announced it one evening, telling them that Lord James had asked if I would go with him.

Mother said, "Yes, Lord James wants you to go as his valet."

Dad just looked and said nothing. I had anticipated a problem that suddenly seemed to have evaporated.

Previously, James had asked me about chest and neck measurements. He had said that I might find one or two things useful that he never wore, but they were always just that little too large.

The weekend before going to Venice, James was away in London sorting out some family business so that I only had to cook for Lady Ruth. Keeping her company, too, had become something of a habit, and we often played cards or Scrabble.

The next time I saw James he handed me two very large dark-green carrier bags with 'Gieves & Hawkes' written on them in large gold letters.

Seeing my surprised look, he said, "Your birthday present. Sorry I haven't wrapped them."

"Thank you. The bags are wonderful!"

Did I dare give him a hug? Where was Lady Ruth? She had a habit of appearing suddenly and very quietly.

My hands went into the largest bag, and I pulled out a dark-green blazer made of the softest cloth I had ever touched.

"I thought dark green would suit you better than blue, what with your fair hair and brown eyes," he said.

Had I ever considered the colour of my own eyes?

"Thank you. It's wonderful," I replied.

Next, I brought out a sports jacket.

"Dogstooth check," he smiled.

When I opened the second bag, there were trousers to go with the jackets, four shirts, two ties and two pairs of brogues.

"I don't know what to say," I began. "I'll have to keep them at the Hall. I don't think I dare take them home – there will be far too many questions."

I walked over and squeezed his hands. If only we had the house to ourselves. Going to Venice with James would be like a dream. I was already nearly as tall as he, so the age difference was not so obvious and I felt quite relaxed with him.

We left for London by rail and travelled first class. We took breakfast in the dining car – most impressive – silver service! A private car took us to the airport. Again we were travelling first class by BOAC and the service was amazing. It was the first time that my feet had ever left the ground – at least in the literal sense – and I could barely take in the wonder of it all.

When we had landed and reclaimed our luggage, a porter was there to take our suitcases to the waiting vaporetto, which was not unlike some of the motorboats I had seen on the Norfolk Broads.

A misty haze was hanging over the water as we sped across the lagoon towards Venice. We had already been handed a glass of champagne, but it was difficult to hold as the boat hit the oncoming swell.

This was beginning to feel like a honeymoon: at least my youthful imagination had always been of two people, deeply in love, celebrating their marriage alone together in some romantic setting. There had been no wedding, but everything else seemed to fit.

As if to announce our arrival, the water slapped loudly against the quay head. A porter was awaiting our arrival and he placed our luggage on a trolley and asked us to follow him to the hotel. James smiled as I gazed in wonder at my surroundings – his smile always melted my heart.

"I really want to kiss you right now," I said.

"You can: we are in Italy and all men kiss." With that he put his hands on both sides of my head and kissed me on both cheeks and then on the mouth. "*Bellisima!*" he shouted.

I could feel the heat rising up my neck and face and I knew that I was changing colour, but when I turned, half expecting a sea of outraged stares, everyone was carrying on as if nothing had happened.

I said, breathlessly, "If that is what we can do, we must live in Italy forever."

James smiled and led me into the magnificent foyer of the Danielli Hotel.

In the next few days, with the sunshine streaming down on us, we seemed to live in an aura of golden light. From our hotel-room windows, we looked across to the magnificence of the Santa Maria Della Salute whilst next door was the pink-and-white confection of the Doge's Palace. One morning James took me to the church of the Santa Maria della Pietà, where, as we walked up the aisle, the most wonderful organ music filled the building. James had discovered that they were practising for a wedding on the coming Saturday. He led me to the altar rail, and as he knelt down he motioned me to follow. He was muttering to himself, and as he finished he looked up and smiled and covered my hands with his on the altar rail. We were still for a few minutes; and as my heart trembled at the thought, I knew that if I was never nearer to marriage than this, no matter. Heaven seemed to have descended as if from one of the magnificent paintings on the ceiling, and I knew that the feeling could never be taken away and would remain with me forever. I didn't feel any sadness when the time came to leave because during those few days our relationship had had time to blossom and I felt more secure in James's love.

We left by the Grand Canal – under the wooden bridge of the Academia and the stone of the Rialto – out across the lagoon to the airport and home.

Easter holidays and school were behind me now. Although my life had changed so much, I think I enjoyed my last weeks at school. The teachers seemed different somehow. Perhaps I had grown up and was more mature.

I had four weeks before going to the City Training College to start my course, and these were to be spent at the Hall. I had now become adept at doing anything from gardening and housework to cooking and waiting. It was even taken for granted that I was quite happy sitting with Lady Ruth to keep her company, which, in truth, I was. By staying at the hall for such an extended period, I had suddenly seemed to become part of it all. What was I going to feel when the time came to move on to a job in a strange hotel or restaurant? Perhaps, after all, I should have trained as a gamekeeper or gardener; then I could have stayed there forever. I was so settled and in love and didn't want things to change.

The time to go to college arrived and a whole new world opened up before me. I had thought that it couldn't be very exciting after all my recent experiences, but it was. I learned so many things so quickly. The days flew by and each Friday evening I moved to the Hall.

Mum was always moaning about not seeing me very much, but my stock reply was "When I am working away in an hotel you won't see me for months."

My love for James and Lady Ruth had grown so much I was beginning to feel that they were more my family than my own.

At the end of the last week of term, I arrived home after seven o'clock and Dad had the bar open already. I was sitting in the back room when James arrived. The bar was full, so Dad had sent him through. I could tell from his face, which was ashen and grey, that he was distressed. He told me that his mother had had a fall and was in bed and was not at all well.

I knew that he had come to see me for comfort, and, before he could ask, I said, "The end of term is here and I've finished my exams. I'll come back to the Hall with you and help."

He seemed greatly relieved, so I set about getting together all the things I needed to take with me, and we were off.

We spent that evening together and I stayed with him in his room that night. Nobody was in the house except Lady Ruth, and she was confined to her room. The Doctor had been and gone and told her she must stay in bed. We had both realised how fragile she had become since the death of Lord Cameron and were very worried about her. The morning was bright and sunny, and we both took her morning tray up to her bedroom. Lady Veronica had been on the phone to James and had organised a nurse who would be coming in every day to help to wash and dress her mother. We had decided to go up and see her before the nurse arrived in case she was not agreeable.

Her lovely smile greeted us from her bed, and we plumped up her cushions and propped her up and told her the news from Lady Veronica. She smiled again and said that she thought it was a good idea as long as she liked the nurse. Wryly, she said that whatever the nurse was like, it would be better than having Veronica around all day.

I served her some coffee and handed her a plate of toast.

The nurse was called Miss Bright, and how appropriate that name was! She was bright and breezy and a real tonic for Lady Ruth. Her presence helped enormously: she came in at eight thirty and got Lady Ruth washed and dressed ready to have her breakfast by nine thirty. James and I would then carry her down to the drawing room or conservatory, and she enjoyed the summer tremendously. She secretly loved being waited on by us both.

When James was busy with the farms, I would read to her or, often, we would just chat or play records. As the summer drew to a close, she was becoming frailer, and one afternoon, when James was away, she had a Mr Pointer in for afternoon tea. He was the family solicitor and must have been nearly the same age as Lady Ruth. A round man with beaming face and bald head, his wire-rimmed glasses made him look like a character from a Dickens novel. He was so kind when I let him in and I guessed that he had already been informed how I fitted into the household. I took him into the drawing room and went off to fetch the tea tray, which I left with them, having told Lady Ruth that I would be in the greenhouses for the next hour or so.

As I walked back after potting up some carnations, I could hear a car on the gravel drive, and then I heard Mr Pointer shouting in a loud, cheery voice from his open window, "Goodbye. See you again."

When I had washed my hands, I went to the drawing room to take the tray away and found Lady Ruth beaming with pleasure.

"Robin, come over and sit down, please. Now, this is our secret – nobody else is to know. Mr Pointer does, of course. He has sorted it out for me." Looking a little serious, she continued: "I have a portfolio of shares, which were given to me by my father. That's his portrait in the hall. They have never been touched. Mr Pointer has held them for me in his safe. Neither Lord Cameron nor his family knew anything about them. I have instructed Mr Pointer to transfer them into your name. They are for you to do with as you wish. Of course, Mr Pointer will help you to understand how to deal with them. I would also be greatly relieved if you would always be available if James has any problems. I know he thinks the world of you. He doesn't realise his mother can see the way he is. I don't think he will get much help from his sisters, although his nephews, when they are older, might be of some help."

I did not know what to say.

The "Thank you" I offered seemed so inadequate that I leaned forward and kissed her on the cheek. As I did so, I saw a tear fall slowly down her face.

Composing herself, she continued: "Mr Pointer knows everything and he will always be there to help you if you have any problems. He has looked after the family's affairs for so long that he seems to be a part of us all."

James came home that evening in a very merry mood. I thought perhaps he was in on our secret, but no, he had had a couple or more drinks on the way home. Were there pressures I didn't know about? Why the drinking?

That evening, as we sat in the sitting room beside the fire, with glasses of port in our hands, he began to tell me of the problems at the bank.

"No money and precious little coming in," he said, staring into the fire.

"The banks are not helping a great deal. We have gone over our overdraft limit for the farms, and it is really getting very difficult to keep it all going." He sighed deeply and sipped his port.

"And now the inheritance tax following Father's death will take a lot of capital, and I don't know that I can raise it. . . ." His voice trailed off into gloomy silence.

Without knowing anything at all about inheritance tax or capital,

I said, "I'm sure things will work out. You have your family solicitor, who has handled these matters for so long."

I looked up to find James fast asleep with his empty glass still in his hand.

Things got no better as the weeks went past. Lady Ruth died in October and James was so depressed that I decided to finish at the college and asked them if I could complete the course the following year because I had family problems. By now they seemed to be as much my family problems as James's. He cheered up remarkably when I told him what I had done.

"You must move out of the wing and into the house and live with me forever." His smile melted my heart.

I knew there would be many difficulties when Lady Veronica arrived for the funeral and her husband followed her blindly for the sake of a quiet life.

"I think he would get crucified if he argued with her," said James, laughing.

"Anyway, the Hall and estate are mine now; and if they don't like you staying here, they can go to hell. Oh," he continued, knowing what I was about to say, "and I won't drink until after the funeral!"

The day of the funeral was wet and cold and, managing to get James alone, I told him, "I think it would be easier if I go with the estate workers." They were carrying Lady Ruth's coffin into the church. "I can then sit with them. Oh, I know you want me to sit with you, but it's your family pew and everybody in the church will think it odd if I'm sitting there."

"But I have asked you to sit with me."

"Can't you see how difficult it could be with all the village there? They will wonder what's going on."

"Let them bloody well wonder," said James angrily.

"Look, James – I love you and I loved Lady Ruth as my own mother, but let's just get this over with, with no fuss and bother from your family. Then we have all the rest of our lives together." I hugged him briefly in case we were disturbed.

As it turned out, they were short of a bearer, so I volunteered and so came to sit in the front row opposite James, who sat in the right-hand side pew with his sisters and brothers-in-law. I knew then how difficult it would have been to sit with James with his sisters so close.

So, all in all, it worked out for the best. I was there and close to Lady Ruth as we carried the coffin out of the church and over to the family plot. As soon as the interment was completed, the family all walked away towards the Hall.

James stayed behind for a short while and I joined him and put my arm around his shoulders. I could see the tears falling from his dark eyes. There was nothing adequate to be said, but I could tell that he knew all that I wished to say.

We knew all at the Hall would be well as Mrs Beeston had arranged a large buffet, sufficient for 200 people, and set it out on trestle tables in the entrance hall. She had also organised ladies from the village to serve the wine and carry the food around. Mrs Beeston, with her weirdly whooping voice and unpredictable cooking, was something of a legend in the village. She was determined that no catering firm should be employed on her territory. She had told James that Lady Ruth had been so good to all the village ladies for the past thirty years that they all wanted to come in to show their respect for her.

This had taken an enormous weight off James's mind as it left him with few things to organise. The ladies virtually took over the whole affair – including the flowers. Even Mr Landamore, the butler, had come out of retirement for three days to look after the guests. He told me, with a particularly kindly look, that I would be far too busy looking after James. I was touched because, in the past, he had always seemed a little aloof when dealing with me.

James lingered on in the churchyard, so I took his arm and gently urged him back across the meadows towards the Hall.

I could see that he had regained his composure, so I volunteered, "I can stay forever if you want me to. I don't have to go back to college and, if you are going to stay on at the Hall, I could help you run the house and garden. We will be able to reduce the staff: Mrs Beeston is getting on and, since she has had the weekends off, she is enjoying her free time. In any case, I think she will be handing in her notice now that your mother has gone." He gave me a quizzical look, but I continued: "You always said you didn't like her cooking." I was fired up now and went on: "Fred is at an age when I think he is ready to give up the garden. I think he only stayed on after your father died for Lady Ruth's sake. He loved her dearly and was always talking about her in the garden, saying what a wonderful woman she was. I am sure that if there are any occasions when we need them to come in, they will do so willingly. Your mother and father were so good to them all and they hold such fond memories of the family that you can be sure they will always be ready to help."

What with all the talking, we found that we had almost got back to the Hall, and, as we entered, all seemed to be going well. People were talking in small groups and the jovial Mr Pointer was holding court with Lady Veronica and the Honourable Daphne. Lady Veronica, who had come purely for the funeral, intended to leave as soon as Mr Pointer had read the will. Daphne and her family were staying overnight before leaving the next morning for the City Airport and the flight back to Scotland. Her two sons, Angus and Frazer, had arrived at the Hall directly from their boarding school by train and taxi.

The buffet was drawing to a close and Mrs Beeston and the village ladies were clearing the tables. Local mourners and distant family were quietly saying their goodbyes to James and his sisters. This was the time for me to make myself scarce and get back to my beloved greenhouses. Their warm and womb-like atmosphere never failed to cheer me up, and the perfume of the flowers seemed to make it the perfect place for daydreaming.

I was sitting on the bench enjoying the peace, and thinking of nothing in particular, when: "Robin, Robin," and Angus and Fraser came bursting in, very red-faced.

"We have been looking for you everywhere," Angus blurted out.

And Frazer chipped in, "Mr Pointer wants you to come to the

dining room. He is reading the will in ten minutes."

"He doesn't want me – I'm not family," I said abruptly.

"Yes, you are definitely to come. He was most emphatic about it," said Angus, gasping for breath from the speed with which they had rushed to find me.

"OK," I said, "give me two minutes."

And off they went, like two demented greyhounds.

I went thoughtfully to the end of the greenhouse and picked up my jacket, which I had left lying on the bench. What was all this about? I just hoped that Lady Veronica had left – her sarcasm towards James made me feel so angry.

As I arrived at the dining-room door, I could see Mr Pointer bustling about, getting everybody seated at the great dining table. Lady Veronica's venom was almost tangible, but my anxiety eased a little when I caught sight of James's face.

Catching sight of me in the doorway, a smiling Mr Pointer called out to me, "Robin, would you like to take a seat? You are mentioned in the will."

I could tell without looking that all eyes were on me, and when I did look up it was to an icy glare from Lady Veronica. All was eerily quiet as I made my way to the table. Fortunately there was a chair next to James and he smiled reassuringly as he pulled it out for me to sit down. The two boys, standing by the sideboard, were grinning like Cheshire cats. They, of course, had overheard the conversations between their parents and other members of the family about Robin and just why he was living at the Hall. Mr Pointer ran through various minor items, pointing out that, as James had already inherited the bulk of the estate under the terms of his father's will, what he would be announcing would be Lady Ruth's instructions as to the disposal of her personal possessions. It seemed that Veronica and Daphne were each to get an item of their mother's jewellery – each was clearly described, presumably to avoid any confusion or argument. I could hear chattering from Veronica, and turned to look at her cold face. Why did she arouse such feelings of hatred in me?

The two grandsons, Frazer and Angus, were each to receive

£10,000 to be held in trust until their twenty-fifth birthdays. Clearly, Lady Ruth's hand was at work here, making sure that their parents did not squander it. By the age of twenty-five their educations would be complete and they should be mature enough to know how to deal with it.

All Lady Ruth's pictures and furniture which had belonged to her own side of the family had been left to James, and, as Mr Pointer announced this, I could feel the tension in the room rising. They were all waiting for the mention of my name. It was obvious from the expression on James's face that he was equally curious. It surely could not be money which had been left to me. I knew from what James had told me that there was little in the bank, and £20,000 had been disposed of to the two boys.

James had told me once, when his mother was out and he had shown me the family jewels, that they were insured for £30,000, which seemed an incredible sum of money. Lady Ruth had already given three pieces to James to give to his wife, if he should marry. I had no idea of their value, but as they were obviously the most important pieces in her collection it seemed that her two daughters had not done too well from the will.

"Robin."

Every head in the room turned towards Mr Pointer as he uttered my name.

"Lady Ruth told me that she considered you to be one of the kindest people she had ever met. She said that her last years had been made particularly happy and comfortable by your being around the house, and, knowing how much you have come to love the Hall and the estate, she has bequeathed Park Lodge to you for your lifetime with rights to come and go over the estate."

He paused for a moment. I did not dare look around, but kept my eyes firmly fixed on Mr Pointer. The family did know that the lodge belonged to Lady Ruth personally, it being a wedding present from Lord Cameron. It was not, of course, included in the estate when Lord James inherited it.

He carried on: "I may say that the contents of the lodge are included in the bequest. After your lifetime, then the property will pass to Angus and Frazer or their heirs." He caught my eye and smiled.

The fury on Lady Veronica's face as I looked towards her told the whole story. She obviously knew that it belonged to her mother and had clearly expected it to come to her. Now she had nowhere to stay in this part of the country, knowing, as she certainly did, that James would not have her in the Hall again.

Mr Pointer folded his papers as he looked over at James and me, and with a beaming smile said, "That is all, Lord James."

I felt, from his obvious pleasure, that he might have had a hand in this conspiracy! James grabbed my hand, and I could tell from his face how happy he was.

Lord Michael Woodhouse came over to me as Veronica gathered up her coat and left the room.

"Thank you for all you have done for Lady Ruth. And do look after James – you know he is not very well."

I smiled and said, "Thank you. I will certainly do that."

As he turned and left the room, I had the feeling that I would never see them again, but what he had said left an uneasy feeling in my mind. Was James unwell or was it just too much drinking? Suddenly Mr Pointer was at my side.

"Goodbye, Robin. I shall be in touch shortly. Do take care of James."

The evening was spent in a strangely subdued atmosphere. We all went to the kitchen to get what we needed to eat. Daphne, obviously still upset by the day's events, was pleasant to me whilst Simon, her husband, engaged James in a long conversation about beef cattle.

I overheard him say, "Get in Aberdeen Angus and get rid of the milking herd – more money, less work."

The boys had gone for a swim and intended to play billiards afterwards. No one mentioned Veronica, but I told Simon and Daphne how pleasant Michael had been and how he had thanked me for helping Lady Ruth.

"He's not a bad sort really," replied James.

Later that evening, in James's bedroom, he lay sprawled across the bed with a brandy in his hand.

"You know, Mother was very fond of you and I'm glad she gave you her special place – she always called it that. She would escape there when the noise of us children got too much for her, or she had had an upset with Father – always to Park Lodge for a couple of days. Nanny had to look after us, and we were never allowed to go there. It was her haven and now it is yours. Will you keep it on?" he asked.

With that, he grabbed me and kissed me, and the next thing I heard was "Uncle James, Uncle James."

As I opened my eyes, I could see the two boys framed in the doorway of the bedroom. It was eight thirty in the morning and they were ready to leave. Thank God we had fallen asleep in our clothes.

James said, "We came up to talk about the estate last night, but we were so tired we must have fallen asleep."

"Well, get up because Mother and Father are waiting for the taxi to take us to the station. We mustn't miss the train or we'll never get to the airport on time."

"We're coming straight down, so buzz off and tell your mother not to worry."

We quickly splashed water on to our faces and passed a comb through our hair, and in no time at all were bounding downstairs to see them off.

We all said our goodbyes, and Frazer said, "What about Christmas?"

"We will arrange it with your mother later," James replied.

"Oh, goody!" they yelled as they were bundled into the taxi.

"We will call you as soon as we get home," Daphne called.

With that the taxi sped off down the drive far too quickly for comfort, and they were gone.

And so we were alone – time to think and plan. What would the future hold? We sat alone in the kitchen sipping our coffee, and my mind ranged over the past twenty-four hours. Here we were, James at twenty-four with the Hall, the Home Farm and two others to manage. I had nothing, but was willing to do anything to help. Thank God for Mr Pointer – he would sort out the finances to enable us to keep things going. I seemed to have enough energy for four people – perhaps love does that to you! Next week, when things had settled down a little, we would need to try to get things sorted out.

On Tuesday Mr Pointer arrived, his arms full of papers tied with red ribbon.

"These are all the estate papers, and I've been to the bank to get your accounts." His face assumed a more serious expression and he sighed.

"Fine – come into the dining room," said James. "There's more room on the table and we can spread all that stuff out."

Soon all the files and other documents were sorted into neat piles on the table.

"Things are not as rosy as I had thought," said Mr Pointer.

"Yes, I knew the farms were not making much profit," James replied. "I don't think they are making any money at all. Perhaps we might think of leasing them out – it might help."

Cheering up a little, Mr Pointer said, "Yes, I'm sure that will be possible. Let me see what can be done."

"Or perhaps we could sell them," James said suddenly.

Mr Pointer was obviously taken aback by this proposal.

"I'm sure that there is no need for that. Let's see about the possibilities of renting them first." He tried to look reassuring, but I could see signs of uncertainty in his expression. "Look here – you are not indebted to anybody, but you have little or nothing in the bank."

"I'm sure that there will be no need for all that," said James. "I would rather sell the farms than have people tramping around my home. But I don't mind the idea of opening up the gardens."

"Well, that's that, then," Mr Pointer said, getting heavily to his feet. "First we will try to rent out the farms. If we are successful, that should bring in enough to keep the estate going. If that doesn't work out, we will sell one farm at a time, and that, I think, will secure everything. Thank you for coffee. I shall go and see what I can do and telephone you in the next few days. Don't despair, my boys."

He gathered up his papers and was soon bustling out of the front door and into his old car.

I walked over to James and, giving him a hug and a gentle kiss on the forehead, whispered, "Now, don't worry. Let's just take it quietly for the next few days until we hear from Mr Pointer, and then we can get to work in earnest."

The whole week was becoming too much for James; what with the loss of his mother, the farms not doing as well as they should and the lack of capital, it was looking more and more likely that he might well lose his home as well. In the circumstances, it was not surprising that he might have developed an ulcer. I decided to get him to Dr Foggarty as soon as I could.

Christmas was fast approaching and it was still not clear who, if anyone, would be coming to stay for the holidays. I saw Mum and Dad occasionally and had told them that I had been given job training as an estate manager. The prospect of a good job kept them happy and they obviously thought I was getting a good wage. What they did not know was that I had not had any money for several weeks before Lady Ruth's death. There was not much hope of anything either.

It turned out that the family would not be coming for Christmas, but the two boys would be coming to stay after Hogmanay and before going back to boarding school.

The year 1966 did not start well: Mr Pointer had not been able to find anybody prepared to rent any of the farms at anywhere near a reasonable rent. James told him not to worry.

"Put Hall Farm on the market and get the best price possible. It's smaller and less productive than Park Farm and should bring in enough cash to keep the estate running for a few years."

Pointer said that he would get it valued and place it with the estate agents.

James seemed to get more and more depressed, but, as I took over more and assumed more control, we had many happy hours getting the garden in trim and redecorating some of the rooms in the Hall; but the thought of selling any part of the estate was not helping James.

Another February and another birthday. My North Star and all the goodies that accompanied its arrival seemed a dim memory. I was seventeen, and a lifetime seemed to have passed in the last eighteen months. I had planned a quiet evening in the dining room and had mentioned to James that morning that it would be black tie at dinner; so there we were, the two of us, in full evening dress with four candelabra burning between us. I had cooked a meal earlier and arranged the dishes on hotplates on the serving table. The dining table I had piled high with flowers and the family silver, and it gleamed softly in the candlelight.

"James, if people were to arrive at this moment they would think we had gone dotty," I said.

"I think you have," he replied.

"Well, it is my birthday," I laughed.

"My God, I forgot! Forgive me." And he got up and came the length of the table and gave a hug which almost crushed the breath from my body.

"No, I know you haven't really forgotten – you've kept me in suspense all day."

Then, I could see from his face that he had indeed forgotten.

Quickly I tried to cover his embarrassment by saying, "Well, at seventeen I think I must forget about birthdays, and I've had so much in the last four years."

At that moment, Bella, who had somehow sneaked in from the drawing room and crept under the table, placed a paw on my knee.

"There's one of my presents. See – she knows it is my birthday and has come to join us. It takes a lot to get her away from the drawing-room fire."

"Now, that is special," said James quietly; and with that, we kissed and silently carried on with our meal.

Later we sat in darkness, except for the glow of the fire. Bella was between us, stretched full length across the hearth. She was the only dog allowed indoors. Of course, I had ruined her as a gun dog, as James, when he wanted to annoy me, often pointed out. My thoughts were racing; things were getting worse, what with nobody wanting to rent the farms and now the possibility of having to sell. I thought perhaps I should talk to Mr Pointer about our shared secret – the bundle of shares. What were they worth? Perhaps they could help. I decided to contact him and ask him to get them valued.

James left early next morning as he wanted to talk to the cowman. I think he intended to ask his advice about selling the milking herd and perhaps trying Aberdeen Angus for beef.

Taking advantage of his absence, I picked up the phone and dialled Mr Pointer's number.

"Pointer speaking."

"Hello, Mr Pointer. It's Robin speaking."

"Robin! It's good to hear from you. Are you both well? How can I help you?"

"Yes, quite well, thank you. I have been wondering about those shares that Lady Ruth so kindly gave me. Can you get them valued because I think they might help with some of our problems?"

"Yes, but do be careful not to mention them to any of the family because, although they were transferred quite correctly before Lady Ruth died, there might be some tax payable. Only you and I know about them, and we must keep it that way. I shall call you next week. Do give my regards to James." And with that the phone clicked off.

James came in at lunchtime seemingly somewhat happier than when he left after breakfast. Apparently, Mr Gott, the cowman, had understood the problem with the milking herd and said that, if it would help, he would willingly stay on and run the beef herd. He told James that, if that was not what James had in mind, he could easily get another job locally with a milking herd. James knew that he had a good reputation thereabouts and had no intention of losing him if he was happy to stay. James told him that he would keep him informed of any developments and left feeling a good deal happier than of late.

Mr Gott had taken the opportunity of letting James know that two of the other cowmen wanted either to go on part-time or retire completely. They had all worked for Lord Cameron for forty years and were now at a time of life when they wanted to take it easier. Most of them had joined the estate when Lord Cameron took it over and, now that he was gone, most of them thought it was time to move on. Mr Gott was anxious that James understood that it was not because he had taken over, but just that they felt that they had done their bit to keep the estate going and really felt too old to cope with any changes that might be coming.

When James had finished telling me about the farm he said, "I've been to see Mr Pointer this morning."

I was slightly taken aback and hoped that it was nothing to do with my conversation with the old solicitor about the shares.

"We should get about £48,000 for the farm. As you know, the farmhouse needs quite a lot of work and the land is mostly pasture and water meadows. There's very little arable land and it's that that holds the real value."

"If you are asking for my advice, James, I would go ahead and sell if you can get that price. We know that several other local farms are having a hard time to make ends meet, and at least we shall have some capital with which to work on the rest of the estate."

That summer of '66 seemed to be perfect. We jogged along; money was a bit scarce, but James kept reminding me we could live on love. In any case, we had some good crops in the gardens and orchard and so had to buy very little.

Nobody seemed interested in the farm, and Mr Pointer advised James to reduce the asking price to £40,000. It was then that I decided to phone Mr Pointer again.

"Mr Pointer, good morning. You never came back to me about the value of those shares Lady Ruth gave to me."

"Yes, yes," he said, stuttering slightly. "I know that it has been rather a long time, but there were a lot of searches to be done. Some of the shares are pre-1948 Russian stocks. I'm afraid we're not getting very far with them. The American Railroad stocks must have been Lady Ruth's grandfather's – he was an American." He coughed a little before continuing: "Good news, though, on one block of shares in a company called Poseidon – an Australian mining company. They have recently struck a rich vein, and if we sell these now at the current market price it should net you about £50,000."

I stood shocked and gulping, and the hand holding the phone dropped to my side. Could it really be that we had this kind of money whilst James was worrying so much?

"Did you say £50,000?" I asked, hardly daring to listen to the reply.

"Yes, yes. The letter only reached me this morning, and I intended to give it a couple of days thought before contacting you."

"But that's wonderful. I can sell some of them and give the money to James." I was in such a state of excitement at the possibility that I could hardly contain myself.

"Robin, just wait a moment and take some advice. I had a feeling that this would be your reaction. This is what I think you should do. I will sell some of the shares and, with the money raised, you should buy the farm; there is no need for James to know who the new owner is. When the sale is completed, I will arrange for it to be rented out. This way James will have the money and you will have secured the farm for the estate. If you give the money to him he will only attempt to keep the farm going and the money will soon be gone. I am also quite certain that, if you tell him about the shares and that you are the new owner of the farm, he will not accept it. He will say that his mother intended you to have the money for helping her."

"But I thought you said that you were having difficulty finding a tenant."

"That was so, but during the last few days we have had a couple of enquiries and I am certain that I could get a reasonable rent, considering the condition of the farmhouse."

"Well, Mr Pointer, please get it all arranged as quickly as possible, and thank you for all your help and advice."

"Goodbye, Robin. I shall be in touch."

"Goodbye, sir, and thank you again."

This should, it seemed, sort out all our problems and take a great weight off James's shoulders.

By Christmas 1966, we seemed to be getting the whole estate

sorted out. James's depression seemed to have lifted after the sale of Hall Farm. The £36,000 he received after tax and the various fees had gone a long way towards restoring the rest of the estate. He had retained the shooting rights over Hall Farm, so I think he felt that he had not lost it completely.

We had some good weekends with some of his university friends staying at the Hall, and his nephews came for most holidays. During the summer, his sister Daphne and Simon had stayed for a few days. She was rather shocked to hear that the farm had been sold, but then she had also been surprised when she knew how little money had been left after her mother died. It was only when they heard about the farm sale that they fully realised what a struggle James had had. I noticed, too, that they had warmed to me – especially Daphne, who had always been pleasant, but a little distant. Her husband had been friendly from the first time we met, and the boys loved to come and roam over the house and grounds. In fact, we felt a bit like brothers.

Simon had been very successful in his business and had offered James money as soon as he realised it was in short supply, but James had thanked him and told him that he was OK now that Hall Farm had been sold. Not easily put off, Simon had told James if he ever considered selling Park Farm to let him know, as he was very anxious to buy it for the boys. James told him that he certainly would let him have first refusal and the matter was dropped.

Just after Christmas, James had organised the sale of the dairy herd to a distant cousin who lived in Northamptonshire and had contacted James when he heard of his plans to sell. He also wanted all the dairy equipment from the milking parlour. Most important of all, he had offered a job and a cottage to Mr Gott, the cowman, if he was prepared to move. It didn't take Mr Gott long to realise on which side his bread was buttered, and after a brief chat with his wife, and much to James's delight, he accepted. Mr Gott had been with the herd since James's father had started to build it up years before, and he knew all there was to know about every beast in the herd. All this was done with the minimum of fuss, and soon James was looking forward to arranging the purchase of pedigree

Aberdeen Angus cattle to start his beef herd. He was to attend a special sale to be held in Cumbria in March. Lord Rowlandson, an old friend of James's father, was selling up, and there was never likely to be a better opportunity to buy good stock.

Unknown to James, Hall Farm, which I had bought with his mother's money, had been rented out at a much lower rent and was secured to come back into the estate when all was running smoothly again.

We spent Christmas alone, with roaring fires and lots of festive food. All seemed well with the world. We had had a sprinkling of snow on Christmas Eve, but on Boxing Day it snowed with a vengeance and by mid morning there must have been a good ten inches. Thank God the milking herd had gone and we were left with only a few sheep on the estate. As these had already been brought into the barns ready for lambing, and the geese had been sold for the Christmas market, there was no need to worry about how much snow would fall.

Simon, Daphne and the boys arrived for New Year's Eve. Much to James's surprise, they had all wanted to come for the holidays. With a few of James's friends arriving, the house had a wonderful festive feel and we all saw in 1967 with fireworks and a great deal of fun and laughter.

A sunny New Year's Day was followed by another sunny day and we were awakened on the third day of January by the boys bursting into our bedroom at 7 a.m., screaming that water was pouring through their bedroom ceiling. After scurrying into our clothes, we were on their tails back to the wing.

The ceiling of the boys' room looked like a rain cloud with water cascading down. It didn't take us long to realise that the weight of the snow must have damaged the roof. The thaw had done the rest.

James shouted, "We had better get up there and have a look."

I said to the boys, "Go and get as many buckets from the laundry as you can find and get them up here and under the holes in the ceiling. That way we may stop the water going through to the next floor."

"I'll ring Jones in the village – he knows all about the lead." And, with that, James was off.

The boys came back with a few buckets and placed them under the worst leaks.

"If you go to the old dairy, you'll find some milk churns. They will hold a lot of water."

Before I could tell them to be careful as they carried them up the staircase, they were off with whoops of delight. It's amazing how disasters for adults are always great adventures for children.

By eleven o'clock, things were not looking too bad. We found a few patches on the ceiling of the billiard room, and some plaster had come down into the swimming pool, where, fortunately, most of the water had ended up. Mr Jones arrived and did some temporary repairs to the roof, and by evening all was relatively quiet again.

I noticed that James had rather more wine than usual, and soon he was on his second brandy.

"We shall have to wait to see how bad it all is until the lead specialist has been," he said, slumping into an armchair. Then James, suddenly startling us all, said, "Isn't it amazing how, just as everything is going along swimmingly, something else comes along and knocks you back again."

I could see Simon willing Daphne not to say anything, so I replied, "You mustn't worry too much. You have a bit of cash now, so you can soon get it put right."

"I'm afraid there's not too much left after all the repairs we've been doing, and I need a little more to go with the money from the dairy herd to pay for the Aberdeen Angus." His face darkened as he considered what the future might hold.

"We will manage somehow. I'm going to make some Ovaltine and at least we have dry beds to go to!" I laughed as I went to the kitchen.

As the family were finishing breakfast, Simon once more offered James any money he might need, but James didn't want to owe money to anybody. The thought of being in debt always worried him in case they might have a claim on his beloved home.

All was quiet and we had the Hall to ourselves again. Time to start to sort out the bedrooms: carpets to be dried out, curtains to be cleaned and a hundred other things to be done. Not that I minded. It was always best to be busy – things calmed down more quickly then. At least they did until Mr Crouch, the roofing specialist, arrived with his men to inspect the roof. We knew before he stepped off the bottom rung of the ladder that we had a big problem.

Looking very concerned, he said, "I'm afraid, Lord Janney, that the roof is in a very bad way. The whole roof of the wing will need replacing very soon. I'm sure you will want to get another opinion and another quotation for the work."

James said, "It is much as I feared. I don't think anything major has been done in the last 100 years. I'm sure you are right, so let me have a price for doing the work as soon as possible."

"I have already measured up and, as long as there is no rot in the roof timbers, you are looking at about £12,000," he replied.

James looked ashen as he said, a little too lightly, "I think we all need a drink. Come into the Hall."

All this was going to be a terrible drain on the capital we had put aside, even if we had that amount left. By the time Mr Crouch and I had caught up with James, he had already opened a bottle of champagne and poured three glasses.

Smiling, he said, "We might as well enjoy what's left of this. There won't be much more!"

"I'm sure it can't be as bad as all that," said Mr Crouch with a worried look.

"Oh, somehow we will manage." I tried to sound reassuring, but failed miserably in the attempt.

The champagne, at least, was doing the trick and James was mellowing visibly.

"It's not too bad, Mr Crouch. You'd better get on with it as soon as possible."

He replied, "I'll get it covered with tarpaulins tomorrow and then we can get at it next week, Lord James."

The champagne had taken effect on Mr Crouch too: it was now Lord 'James' and not Lord 'Janney'. But then, it was obviously having an effect on us all because we chatted in high spirits for several minutes and I thanked heaven for the power of alcohol and how it would help for a few hours.

Another birthday, and a quiet one – at least as quiet as it could be with four workmen on the roof with hammers and blowtorches, crashing their ladders and shouting to each other above the general din.

James had not bothered to get another quotation. His father had used Mr Crouch's firm on all his buildings for forty years. It is amazing how loyal landed families are to the firms they use and the workmen they employ. There seems to be a bond of trust, which doesn't always apply elsewhere in the community.

By the end of February, the sun was shining on the new lead roof, now safe and sound for another 100 years. In the Hall, the plaster ceiling on the ground floor had dried out and the absence of staining was a great relief to both of us. To our great dismay, the original quotation had risen from £12,000 to £20,000 because the removal of the old lead had revealed dry rot and death-watch beetle. James was praying that there might be grant monies available because this expenditure had made serious inroads into the beef-cattle money and the sale was looming a month ahead.

The following Monday morning, James came bursting into the kitchen, his face beaming.

"I've been to see Mr Pointer with the bank manager and they have organised a £20,000 loan against the deeds of the estate, so we can now go ahead and buy our cattle."

I smiled and said, "That's wonderful news," but my thoughts were full of the fact that before too long it would have to be paid back, and that would probably mean the sale of the rest of the portfolio of shares.

But James knew nothing of this.

We had a wonderful trip north. The weather was fine and sunny and we stopped for food here and there along our route in wonderful old pubs. This part of the country was entirely new to me, and I enjoyed every minute of the journey. James had booked us in at the local Trust House Hotel, which had incredible oak beams and very old furniture. I confess that I thought the food needed to be improved, but then I'd been spoiled since being a child.

James got what he wanted at the sale: thirty breeding Aberdeen Angus cows. Now all we needed was a couple of bulls, and he had been told by a farmer at the auction of a gentleman farmer near Leicester who had one or two for sale. Arrangements were made for us to call on our drive south. The cattle we had already purchased were to be transported the following week, so we expected to be well and truly home before they arrived in Norfolk.

Mr Colby's farm was situated about five miles outside Leicester, and it was obvious as we drove up the long drive to the house that here was an exceptionally well-maintained property. The house – a beautifully proportioned Georgian country residence – nestled into the rolling countryside surrounded by mature oaks and elms. James sighed at the sight of it, and I knew that he was thinking of just how much work remained to be done on his own home.

Mr Colby himself turned out to be a large, pleasant man of sixty or so with a healthy red face and a nose with a wart on the tip of it. He took an instant liking to James, and we all got on very well. Lunch had been laid on, and after a pleasant hour or so we were taken down to the cattle sheds and introduced to the foreman. James selected a couple of fine beasts and was anxious to know about the animals' pedigree. He was shown the records, which seemed to go back forever: Colby's family had owned the land for nine generations, and he took a great pride in his stock.

"No need to worry about that, my boy," he said. "They'll come with full documentation and in prime condition. Just make sure you're ready to receive them in a couple of weeks' time. I'll telephone to let you know exactly when."

It is always good to be back at home and, almost before we arrived, James went down to the cattle sheds to check that his instructions for cleaning them had been carried out whilst we had been away. I could tell from his face, when he returned to the house, that all was well.

The pastures, too, were looking at their best: the milking herd had not been on them during the winter months to churn them up, and so, on the appointed day when the cattle arrived, we were quite ready to receive them. Our excitement was intense when we turned them out on to the pastures, looking magnificent, their black coats gleaming in the sunlight. James was now all smiles and was a delightful companion.

The depression of the past few months was behind him and he seemed to have shed ten years when he said, with a smile, "A good year's breeding, and we should have made enough to pay off the loan. Then it should be plain sailing."

As I nodded and grinned, I thought that with my money coming in as well we should be fine.

A few days later, the bulls arrived to be followed, shortly after, by Mr Kemp. James had employed him as a specialist Aberdeen Angus man, but he could turn his hand to just about anything on the farm.

"These are the sort of people to have on the farm: they have a specialist knowledge but are willing to tackle any job you can throw at them."

Two of the old hands had asked to leave and, with Kemp insisting that he could manage alone, the wages bill had, if anything, gone down a few pounds. This was going to be a much better deal on a small farm.

March was kind and warm. The daffodils around the Hall and up the drive were at their best and the whole place looked like a picture postcard. March went out like a lion, but within a few days spring asserted its influence and Kemp was bursting with enthusiasm. He told James that most of the cows had been inseminated, but at least eight must have been done before they arrived because they were already carrying calves. It was a great joy to James, and he radiated good humour. Life was becoming very settled and the love we had for each other had become very strong.

The running expenses, apart from the roof, were now under control, and, as Mr Pointer said, when he came for lunch just before Easter, "James, I really think you have turned the estate around. If you get a good beef sale next year it could clear everything. Corn prices are also up, and with your new crop of mustard for Colman's, all looks well for the future."

"I do hope so. Things have been a bit tough these past eighteen months, but we seem to be managing. Have a glass of port. Come to think of it, we may even be able to put down a few bottles in the cellar. There isn't much left of what Father laid down."

"Yes, yes, splendid idea! Here's to you both." And he beamed his beaming smile.

May Day fell on a Monday morning and we were tucking into a splendid breakfast of bacon and eggs. The eggs came fresh from the bantams, which roamed around the stable block. At this time of the year, eggs could get rather scarce because most of the hen birds disappeared into unknown parts of the estate to sit on clutches of eggs. Then, pretty well all through the month of May, they reappeared with large broods of fluffy chicks behind them – sometimes as many as twelve at a time. We had hardly laid down our knives and forks when there was a loud banging on the kitchen door. Before we could get across the kitchen to open the door it burst open and Mr Kemp entered, looking very worried indeed.

"I'm sorry to barge in like this, Lord James, but I think we have a big problem. I think you had better come down to the sheds. Some of the cows are foaming at the mouth. You'd better call the vet before you come, sir."

"Yes, right away."

And James dived into the hall to the phone. No more than a minute later, he was back.

"The vet is coming right away, Mr Kemp. We will follow you in the Land Rover."

And with that we pulled on our wellington boots and made for the door. In a couple of seconds, rather than taking the drive, we were tearing across the front meadows to gain a little time.

The affected animals were standing very still, a bubbling froth falling from their mouths. Two had their tongues hanging out.

"Lord James, I think it could be foot and mouth," Kemp said quietly. "I heard, at six o'clock this morning on the farming programme, that there has been an outbreak in Leicestershire, but so far it is unconfirmed."

"God, no. This can't be happening – not this far away in Norfolk."

"The bulls might have been carrying it when they came from Mr Colby's."

"No, no!"

I could see that James was beginning to get very angry, and he turned and walked away a few steps. As he did so we heard the roar of a diesel engine and soon the vet's car appeared.

The battered old car pulled up beside us and John Lindley, the vet, got out. There was no mistaking Lindley as his dress rarely changed: old tweed plus-fours, heavy Norfolk jacket, brogues and a flat cap. Before I could finish the thought that the brogues were hardly suitable for the mud which surrounded us, he had whipped them off and donned a pair of wellingtons.

His rather gruff "Good morning, Your Lordship," and his brief nod to Kemp and me, showed that he clearly had no time for niceties in the face of the possibilities he had come to explore.

"I hope to God it's not what you think it is. I've heard that it started further north; but if precautions aren't put in train very quickly, it will spread like a bush fire. All the necessary systems should be in place to contain it. Now I'll take some swabs and get them back to the labs for analysis. Then I must get on to the ministry." He nodded to Mr Kemp. "You'd better get plenty of straw on all the entrances to the estate and soak it well with disinfectant. I know you keep plenty in stock. Then place footbaths at every entrance and put up notices forbidding all vehicles from coming in."

"Right you are, sir." And Kemp was off.

I called after him, "If you need anything at all, at any time, call us at the Hall and we'll be down as soon as possible."

We turned to say our farewells to the vet to find that he had already removed his boots and put on his shoes for driving.

"Try not to worry too much, James. I'll be in touch as soon as I have anything for you." And with that he too was disappearing down the lane, the old car belching oily black smoke.

We walked into the Hall and James made straight for the

74

drawing room and the whisky decanter. Not a good sign, I thought. We often had a glass of wine or a sherry at lunchtime, but this was something new.

"Now, don't say a word. Things have got as bad as they possibly can and I need this to survive."

"Fine, but please don't take too many as we may be needed to help."

It was the best that I could think of to keep him away from the decanter.

"No, I can't do any more. I think this was the last chance for us to get things going – to keep it all together."

And he downed a second glass and moved towards the table. I could tell from his body language that he was completely drained, so I went over to him and hugged him to me.

"Thank you," he said with a weary smile. "I really needed that. You will stay, whatever happens?"

"Always. I've told you that so many times. And even if it gets very bad we have always got Park Lodge. It's a beautiful house and it's on the estate. It is always going to be there whatever happens because it can't be sold. That is, if you can bear to live so close to the Hall and not own it yourself."

"Yes, that would be nice if we have to sell up," he replied.

We were up very early for the next two days, expecting to hear at any moment from the vet. No news came until late on Wednesday afternoon, when Mr Kemp phoned with the news we had been dreading. James had slipped into the village, so I took the call.

"Hello, Lord James? Oh, Robin, it's you. I'm dreadfully sorry to have to be the bearer of such bad news, but Mr Lindley has just contacted me with the lab results and I'm afraid they are positive. The ministry will be sending in men tomorrow to slaughter the herd and arrange for the disposal of the carcases. I'm sorry to say that the sheep will have to go too."

"Thank you, Mr Kemp. I will pass the message on to Lord James. God knows what his reaction will be. I'm glad, at least, that they will not be disposed of on the farm. It would be a constant reminder if they were buried here. Thank you for calling. I'll get Lord James to telephone you later."

In the course of our conversation, Kemp had pointed out that the reason for removing the carcases for disposal was the close proximity of the river and the high water-table level. The ministry could not permit the possible contamination of the water supply.

Before James returned, the phone rang again. It was the vet.

"Hello, Robin. It's Lindley here. Is James about?"

"No. He has gone to the village for an hour or so, but Kemp has already told me the news. James will be devastated."

"I don't envy you the job of telling him. Will you also tell him that the carcases are to be taken away to Morton for disposal? There's been another case there and there are few problems with the water there. Will you tell James how sorry I am? I know he has been hoping for a new start and this will set him back badly. You realise that it will be at least a year after the outbreak is under control before he will be able to restock?"

"I realise all that, Mr Lindsay, and I think this will be too much for him to bear. I don't think he will have the heart to start again."

At that moment I heard the kitchen door slam.

"James is back, so I'll ring off now. I'll get him to ring you a little later, when I've had a chance to break the news more gently."

I put the phone down and turned to face James, who had just come into the drawing room.

"Who was that, Robin?"

"Mr Lindley. Look, James – I'm afraid it's bad news. The results are positive and the herd will have to be destroyed. He has everything in hand and Kemp will deal with the men from the ministry when they arrive tomorrow."

James's face was ashen as he sat down heavily at the table, and for the moment I kept the other details to myself.

"Robin, we're going to have to give some serious thought to our futures. This could all be disastrous for both of us."

"Let's leave any thought of the future until we've got over the next couple of days. Then we can have a few quiet days in the garden and something will come to us. It will give us space to clear our heads and think more clearly."

With the arrival of May there was a real feeling of summer in the air. The southerly winds had been kind and the garden was beginning to bloom. James was still withdrawn and I could see that the loss of the cattle, and the new start they were intended to bring, still filled his thoughts. His intake of alcohol had steadily increased so that the stock of wine which his father laid down was virtually gone. What we particularly enjoyed together was the champagne which his father had bought for James's wedding – an event that was unlikely ever to happen. It certainly helped him to dull the pain of all that had happened and I just hoped that, by the end of the summer, we would be able to forget the whole awful business. By then the cellar would be empty and perhaps we could get back to some sort of normality. It was at this time that I noticed that James's periodic bouts of illness had stopped, but, of course, the symptoms could have been relieved by the drinking.

With the summer over, we had achieved some sort of routine. What with running the Hall and harvesting at Park Farm, we had been too busy to brood over the past. The wages bill was further reduced by the retirement of two more of the older men, and Mr Kemp had gone off to work at another farm in Suffolk, where so far the herd he was working with had been spared the scourge of foot-and-mouth disease.

We had a very happy three weeks at the end of September when a cousin of James appeared unexpectedly. David was the son of one of Lord Cameron's sisters, who had married an American colonel during the war and had gone back to Boston when the war ended. I recalled that Lord Cameron had intended to visit them when his plane had crashed and he had been killed.

David had been wounded on a bombing mission in Vietnam when his plane had been shot down over the Mekong Delta. Luckily they had been picked up almost immediately because a rescue chopper had been in the area trying to locate another pilot, shot down the previous day. His broken leg and arm had been temporarily patched up and he was sent back to Lakenheath American Air Force base in Suffolk, where his broken bones had been reset and he was recuperating, knowing that he had relations nearby. When he was able properly to manage his crutches, he applied for leave and came to stay.

He was a cheerful, good-natured person, always laughing and joking, and he turned out to be a great tonic for us all at the Hall. David's efforts to control his crutches as he hobbled around the estate, and his attempts to swim, caused so much laughter that we were able to forget our own problems and laugh with him. For a while James seemed quite his old self and I was happy for him.

David bought in a fresh supply of wine from the PX Store on the airbase. Everything there was so much cheaper and he was able to get it at less than half the price. I suppose in some ways it was a benefit, but I was anxious that James would now continue to drink too much.

David loved to play the gramophone, and one record in particular was constantly being played – it was a song sung by Don McLean, an American singer whom we had never heard of in Norfolk, or 'in the sticks', as David joked. The record was called 'Nineteen Sixty-Seven' and was about the loss of his friends in the Vietnam War. It seemed to us that David was suffering from the loss of someone very close to him – perhaps one of his buddies who hadn't survived. We thought that, one day, he would tell us about it, but were careful not to press him for information.

When the visit, which went on for two weeks longer than planned, came to an end, David managed to get a flight to an airbase just outside Boston. For him the war was over, but he realised, with so many young men being captured or killed, that he was one of the lucky ones. One evening before he left he was unusually quiet and sad and he told us about the loss of so many of his friends. He said that it was bad enough when he knew they had died, but when they were taken prisoner the thought of the tortures they were subjected to was almost unbearable.

We saw him off from the base on a bright December morning and we knew that we were back to sorting out our own lives once again. Whilst we were away, a letter arrived from Mr Pointer saying that he wanted to see us. James phoned him at once and arranged for him to come to lunch the following Sunday.

The day dawned cold and frosty – I think it was the first real frost we had had that year. During the past few days we had talked ourselves silly about how we were going to manage. The farm had been ticking over nicely and we wondered if we should open the gardens next year to the public. All in all, we really thought we had cracked it.

At eleven o'clock precisely, the doorbell rang and I went to open it.

"Good morning, Mr Pointer," I said as I opened up and let him in.

"A crisp morning, my boy. This will put paid to the last of the late roses."

"Yes, I just hope that it kills off the damned greenfly, which has been plaguing us all summer," said James, who had come into the hall to welcome the old solicitor.

"How are you, Mr Pointer?"

"Quite well, James, thank you, but this sort of weather gets into my old bones."

"Well, I find that hard to believe – you never seem to get a day older. You're just as I remember you when I was a boy."

"That's kind, if somewhat inaccurate." Mr Pointer laughed as he bustled through to the dining room. "I've brought all the papers and collected your accounts from the bank on Friday." His face had become a little more pensive.

"Let's leave all that until after lunch," said James. "I thought we would have a drink at the table. What's it to be – sherry or a glass of wine?"

"Oh, it's always sherry for me. We mustn't spoil Robin's excellent lunch." And he glanced archly in my direction.

I had set the table during the morning and it looked at its best. I had cleaned all the best silver earlier in the week and it gleamed against the beautiful Cuban mahogany of the dining table. We were sitting at one end – the table sat sixteen – so I had made a large floral arrangement which took the bareness off the empty space at the other end.

"You've done us proud, Robin. I love to see a well-laid table."

We sat quietly talking trivia whilst we finished our aperitifs. I had prepared a traditional English lunch of roast beef and Yorkshire pudding, which I knew the old boy loved and so rarely got in his bachelor household. We washed it down with a couple of bottles of burgundy. It was James's favourite lunch, too, and Lady Ruth always produced it for Sunday lunch as soon as the first frosts arrived. I could see that James was thinking of this as he raised his glass to me across the table.

After Mr Pointer had demolished a small mountain of Stilton, I knew it was safe to clear the table; and by the time I had fetched the coffee tray from the kitchen, he had spread out his papers and was waiting for me to join them.

During lunch we had talked of our various ideas for keeping the estate going. Pointer liked to hear all this – I think it gave him a better idea of how to organise our finances and what suggestions he might make which would be in tune with our own ideas. But what finances? What with the roof repairs coming in over budget and the loss of the beef herd, the account was well and truly in the red.

"Of course, you will get some compensation for the cattle, but it will by no means cover the outlay. Then there was your projected profit from the first year's operation, which was meant to cover the management of the estate."

James did not seem to be listening. I could tell by the way he was looking towards the window and out across the meadows that he was thinking of something else. Perhaps he didn't want to hear. There didn't seem much we could do to save what we had. In the back of my mind I knew we had more to come from Lady Ruth's portfolio, but we seemed to have had so much already. Could there be much more? Surely there was not enough to keep everything together. I resolved to speak to Mr Pointer confidentially the next day.

"Well, James, the bottom line is that you owe the bank about £12,000, and with interest rates being what they are it will be considerably more than that this time next year. I don't see much profit coming from the farm until next harvest. With the rest of the farm being grazing land we all knew there's not much profit in that. Even if you were able to afford to restock, the ministry will not permit it until we have been free of this damned disease for at least another six months."

Pointer had really said all that there was to be said. It was now up to James to come up with something to solve our problems. I knew, only too well, how difficult that would be. We lived economically enough. All our food came from the gardens and the surplus was sold to local shops, but the few pounds coming in were a drop in the ocean compared with what was needed to keep up the Hall. James had told me that there were a few interesting pictures around the Hall, but not one of them held any great value, and, in any case, what they were worth would only hold off the inevitable for a little while.

When James looked up to face the old boy, I could tell from his eyes just how much damage this was doing to his health. His eyes were almost as black as the eyebrows above them.

"Well, Mr Pointer, I'll try to sort something out in these next few weeks and have some sort of plan for you by Christmas," he said, but from the tone of his voice I knew there was little hope in his heart.

How I wanted to get up and hug him, but Pointer's presence ruled that out.

James left the house early next morning, and so I was able to phone Mr Pointer just after eight-thirty. I knew that he was always at his desk by eight o'clock in order to get the day started before the office staff arrived.

"Good morning, Mr Pointer. I wanted to speak to you yesterday, but it was not possible in front of James. It's to do with Lady Ruth's shares."

"Yes, Robin, I thought that was going through your mind yesterday. You were wise not to raise the matter then. I will check them out in the next few days. I do know that the value of the rest of the Poseidon shares has risen handsomely, but, even with that, I don't know that it will be enough to save the Hall; and, even if it is, would it be worth it? It may only buy a short reprieve, and then you will be back to square one. I'll speak to you next week. Forgive the rush, but I have a client arriving in a minute or two. Goodbye, Robin."

Christmas arrived once more. No special plans had been made

this year, and we spent it quietly Daphne and the boys all stayed in Scotland and Veronica and her husband joined them there. Some of the American cousins were going to join them, too.

There was some talk of them all coming at the end of January, but nothing definite. At least I had finally persuaded James to make an appointment to see Dr Foggarty, and this was arranged for the first week in the New Year.

James was looking downcast when he returned from the appointment.

"Well, did he tell you what the problem is?" I asked anxiously as James came into the kitchen.

"I'm not sure. I have had some blood samples taken, which are being sent off for testing. Foggarty said I am a bit anaemic and he wanted to have it checked out."

The cousins did not arrive after all. They had left Edinburgh for Paris and Rome – no doubt after a great deal of family gossip. I could just imagine the conversation about James living with the gamekeeper's son! David had not come over from America with the cousins, so we did not miss him, although it would have been nice to see him again – he always cheered James up with his laughter and his limp! Sometimes I felt a little jealous when David was around because he was very handsome and had incredible charm, but, as I told James, that sort of thing does not happen between relations. It always amused James when I told him that David ought really to be my lover. He enjoyed being teased.

Dr Foggarty's news was not good, and an appointment had been made to see Dr Hampton at the General Hospital. It fell on my birthday – 14 February.

In the last few weeks, James had seemed so exhausted and prone to catching every cold or bug that was going the rounds. I was beginning to feel that I should have trained as a doctor. Our relationship was as loving as ever, but everything seemed to get on top of him and bring him down.

When we arrived at the hospital, James spoke to Dr Hampton's secretary to see if I might go in with him. She seemed, at first sight, to be rather formidable, but when she came off the intercom she was smiling.

"That will be quite all right, Lord Janney. You may both go in. Dr Hampton is ready to see you."

As we entered the room, a tall, dapper man of about thirty-five with a fine crop of golden hair rose from behind his desk. I was slightly taken aback. Doctors, in my experience, were always as old as my parents and rather grey.

"Good morning, Lord Janney," he said in a soft, cultured voice.

"Do call me James, and this is my friend, Rob, who lives with me and takes good care of me when I am ill, which is why I asked for him to be with me now."

A lovely smile and a handshake that all but crushed my fingers.

"Good morning, Dr Hampton."

"Paul," he said, and smiled again.

This was a good start. His friendliness would help James to relax, especially as I was half fearing that something more serious was to follow. It also crossed my mind that his easy manner might just indicate that he was of the same persuasion as James and myself.

"James, I have seen the results of your blood tests and Dr Foggarty's notes. Will you take off your shirt so that I can examine you?"

For a minute or two, Paul worked quietly over James's chest and back with his stethoscope before saying, "We shall need to have some X-rays taken, but in my opinion you are suffering from chronic myeloid leukaemia, which affects the white blood cells. I know that this seems very technical, but basically it means that there is an abnormal progressive accumulation of white blood cells throughout your body."

I could see from their expressions that this was very bad news. James had known that he had something wrong with him for almost a year, but had failed to have it checked out despite my pleading with him.

James said, "I thought deep down that it might be something serious and, although it sounds stupid now, that's why I didn't go to see Foggarty sooner. Robin has been telling me for months . . ."

His voice trailed away and he looked very grey.

"Well, it's too late to start worrying about why you didn't come and have it checked out sooner. That's water under the bridge. Most of my patients seem to think that the aches and pains they suffer will just go away if they try to ignore them. I'll arrange for you to come in next week for more tests. We can get you on a course of drugs to try to contain it. I'm only sorry that I could not give you some better news."

"Paul, please don't apologise. I'm most grateful for your time and kindness. I wonder, perhaps, if you might come to the Hall for a bite of lunch or supper? Robin, I know, would love to cook you a meal." And he gave me a knowing smile.

"I would be more than happy to," I said, smiling broadly at Paul. "And thank you for seeing James so quickly."

We all shook hands once more, and Paul ushered us from his office to the reception room.

"I shall look forward to seeing you both again," he called after us.

James was now looking very groggy indeed: his face was ashen and he stumbled as we left the hospital building. We needed to get home fast.

"Let's go straight home, James. We can do the shopping some other time. You've had quite enough for one day."

This was not the time to be dragging around the city.

The journey home was a silent one – we were both deep in our own thoughts: Just how bad was James's illness? How long had we got together? Could anything be done? Our minds were in turmoil.

When we arrived, the Hall was like a warm cocoon, everything so familiar. Nothing seemed so bad now that we were home. As soon as the door closed behind us, I took James in my arms and held him tightly to me.

"We are going to be OK," I told him. "We will sort all this out and get back to normal. Trust me. Go and sit in the drawing room and get warm and I will make some tea."

And I was off to the kitchen with Bella yapping excitedly at my heels. She hated being left at home, but we never took her with us in the car if it meant leaving her for any length of time. James always said that he didn't care if the car was stolen, but he couldn't bear to think of losing the dog.

My nineteenth birthday had gone in a haze.

We both kept busy during the days that followed. James checked the workings of the farm, organising crops and all the other thousand and one things that needed to be taken care of. We spent a lot of time together in the gardens, clearing the leaves from the lawns and driveways. When the weather was too bad, we worked in the Hall sorting out a load of furniture in the wing, which was surplus to requirements, hoping to raise some extra cash at the local auction house.

All this time had passed and I had not thought about the shares or Mr Pointer. I really had to get it sorted out, but it would have to wait until after the hospital visit.

Paul was waiting for us when we arrived.

"Come straight in," he said with a smile.

Was it good news or not?

James said, "I'm afraid we're a little early. Never quite sure about the car parking situation."

"That's quite all right. You are my first visitor, so it will give us a little more time."

'How nice of him to use the word "visitor" rather than "patient"!' I thought.

"Do have a seat. Would you like some coffee?" Paul asked.

"No, thank you, Paul. We both had an enormous breakfast and coffee before leaving, and it's too early for a gin!"

"Even for me," laughed Paul.

I knew that James was trying to be brave – neither of us had any idea quite what to expect. The smile had left Paul's face and his expression was serious as he looked directly at James.

"Well, James, I'm afraid my original diagnosis was correct: it is myeloid leukaemia. The blood samples I took when you were here last show a marked increase in the white-blood-cell count compared with those taken by Dr Foggarty."

James sat silently, staring at a watercolour of Venice on Paul's wall. Was he taking all this in? Paul had gone into some detail about the treatment of the disease, which went quite over my head. Had James even heard him?

Paul continued in his professional manner: "Myeloid leukaemia is unique in its association with a specific chromosome abnormality. There are at least two drugs known to be effective. Both have different toxic effects. They can be given in combination, which increases the therapeutic, but not the toxic, effects." Paul continued: "Of course, all this is why you have been feeling so tired and weak and have been prey to so many colds and other infections. Dr Foggarty told me on the phone that you had had more than your fair share of those." He paused. "We will try a blood transfusion first."

James shifted in his chair and it was obvious that he had been listening despite his apparent distraction, because he looked up at Paul and said, "Will I have to stay in hospital?"

"Yes, we will have you in for a couple of days for the transfusion. When we have seen the effects of that, we can go on from there."

"Paul, if it's as bad as you say it is and I have to be in hospital for a very long time – well, I don't think I could stand that."

"You know, James, that we shall do our best, but it really is a matter of waiting to see how you respond to the transfusion; let's wait and see."

James looked straight at Paul, and I knew from the determined look on his face that he intended to get the information he wanted; it was equally clear that Paul knew the question that was coming.

"Tell me honestly, Paul, for Robin's sake as well as my own, what happens if the transfusion doesn't work?"

"If your condition remains poor, I am afraid that we can measure the time in months – perhaps even weeks. If rapid deterioration and bleeding occur, then we can allay any pain which would normally ensue by the proper use of drugs, but at this point in time, let's be positive. We will start you on a course of busulfan and get you in as soon as we can."

I knew that Paul had taken a great liking to James and that he was finding it difficult to give the information James was demanding, but James pressed on: "How is that taken – by injection?"

"No, just pop them in like Smarties," said Paul, trying to lighten the mood.

I began to feel that the worst part was over, now that Paul had given James the facts. I could see, too, that he was ready for a drink and that it was going to be a brandy rather than a coffee, although he didn't want to stop on the way home. He just wanted to get back to the Hall.

As we neared the entrance lodge to the estate, he said, "If things are still bad financially, I think I will get Pointer to sell the whole estate."

"You mean the Hall as well?" I asked.

"Yes. It's just not worth struggling on. We have a home at Park Lodge."

I could see the sadness and resignation in his eyes.

"Could you live there happily, with the Hall so close and all the memories?"

"Well, if it doesn't work out, there should be enough left over after we have paid our debts to be able to move away. We might even go abroad."

"I don't think that would be a good idea if you need constant medication, but it's too early to decide such things. Let's just wait and see how things develop."

I was beginning to feel a little easier. James was at least thinking positively, which was remarkable considering the shattering news he had just been given.

When we got into the Hall he said, "Look – I'm going to ring Pointer right now. I know we owe the bank a hell of a lot, so I'll get him to have the estate agents value the whole lot. I know that the farm and Hall will have to be sold as one lot, which might just make it easier."

It was at that moment that I made up my mind to go along with any decisions James might make. At least he would be happy, and I would be free of any possibility of giving bad advice. The days ahead were not going to be easy, but at least James would feel he was in charge of his destiny – and mine!

We did finally get a drink, but it was not the brandy I had anticipated. Instead James opened a bottle of champagne. He always loved his champagne and I knew that at this moment he was not likely to worry about how much of it he drank, or what it cost.

As we sat in the conservatory quietly drinking, James leaned across and picked up the phone.

"Good afternoon, Mr Pointer. It's James Janney. Do you think you could give me a couple of hours as soon as possible? If you could make it around lunchtime one day, Robin will cook us a good lunch."

It was clear from the tone of his voice that James had got a grip on the situation and that there was no going back.

He replaced the phone and said, "He's coming tomorrow. We'll give him a good blow-out – you know how he likes his food."

"Good morning, James. Good morning, Robin." Mr Pointer could never disguise his moods and it was obvious that he was in a good one when he arrived the next morning.

"Come into the drawing room, Mr Pointer. I've got a bottle of bubbly already opened."

"A bit early, my boy, but I've never been known to refuse – especially in such pleasant company!" he said with his most engaging grin.

And so we sat and James told his story. He didn't keep anything back, and soon Pointer had all the details of yesterday's diagnosis and James's thoughts about what we should do next.

"Well, I confess that I had my suspicions that all was not as it should be. Lady Ruth often expressed her concerns about your health and, if you'll forgive me, your stubbornness in not getting something done about it."

"Please don't apologise, Mr Pointer. I consider you too old a friend to be mincing words with me. Indeed, I'd go as far as to say you are one of the family."

The old man's eyes moistened as he replied, "Thank you, James. I like to think so too."

"Let's keep it short and sharp," said James. "We have decided that the best thing to do is to sell the whole estate. You know that I love the place, but I don't think I could stand all the worry and heartache trying to keep it all above water. I think you know that my brother-in-law, Simon, offered me financial help, but what would be the point? There would always be the problem of paying it back, and still we would be no further forward." His gaze took in the view from the drawing-room window across the meadows he loved so much as he continued: "Perhaps you can get it valued and give some thought about how best to market it. Ultimately we shall move into Park Lodge, which Mother left to Robin. I can settle up with the bank and, if there is anything left, we can talk about investments later."

"Now, James," said Mr Pointer seriously, "the bank has already had the estate valued when your overdraft reached £10,000. Obviously they had to be prepared in case it became necessary to foreclose, in which case you would have been pushed into a sale. I must say, they have been very good, keeping in touch with me at all times. They know, of course, that I have been acting for the family for many years, and also they were anxious not to trouble you too much after all the problems you have had."

He paused, and I could see from his expression that he was glad that James had raised the question of selling-up. My guess was that was what he had come to tell us anyway, and that he was pleased not to have to take the initiative.

Looking somewhat more cheerful, he continued: "The bank valuation was about £120,000. You understand, of course, that this valuation relates to what they would expect to raise following the sort of quick disposal resulting from foreclosure. They would want to get the property off their hands as soon as possible. Similarly, if you want to sell quickly, the same sort of valuation would apply. My estimation is that by the time you have paid off the overdraft and other debts you will be left with about £85,000. If that is the case, you ought to be able to settle down with a tidy amount of capital and a few less worries."

Mr Pointer sat back in his chair and took another sip of champagne. His relief that he had sorted all this out before he arrived, thus saving any further delays, was obvious to me, but

I think had gone unnoticed by James. We all settled down to a lunch of pot roast – another of Mr Pointer's favourites – secure in the knowledge that, with the decision taken, we could now look more clearly to the future. The only cloud hanging over us now was that of James's health. Would the transfusion be our salvation, or would the next couple of years be long and drawn-out, coping with his illness?

At least all our money worries would be over and there should be enough to carry on living the sort of life that James was used to with money to spare. There was the question, too, of my shares, which I really needed to get sorted out. The income from Park Farm was not very great, so I thought it might be as well to sell that too. The original thought of keeping it so that it could be brought back into the estate was now a thing of the past. It was now up to Pointer to make the necessary arrangements for the disposal of the shares and for me to get to see the old solicitor quietly about my own situation. Things were becoming a little clearer in my mind.

Looking much happier than I had seen him of late, James said, "Thank you, Mr Pointer. You have taken an enormous weight off my mind. Robin and I will now be able to spend some time and thought on how to organise our lives once all this is sorted out. I am very grateful to you – as always."

As I saw Mr Pointer to the car, I said, "Can I pop into the office during the week? I think it is time to cash in the rest of the shares that Lady Ruth gave me."

"Yes, come in on Friday – about three o'clock. I have done a considerable amount of research on those old stocks. The remaining shares have gone up considerably, so this is not a bad time to sell them off. By Friday I should have a very good idea of the sums we are talking about."

We shook hands and he jumped into his car and was off with a wave of his hand and "Thanks for another excellent lunch and the opportunity to see James smiling again."

During the next two days the sun shone and the temperature soared into the eighties. We spent many enjoyable hours in the garden.

James said, "Let's have a final tidy-up and take plenty of

cuttings. We can separate the perennials so that we can take them down to Park Lodge and redesign the gardens there. As you know, the paddock at the side goes with the house and would make a wonderful herbaceous garden. It's enclosed by the North Wood, so it will be very warm and very private."

This was the old James, whom I knew and loved before the loss of his parents and all the subsequent worries. My heart soared.

Friday arrived and I made sure that James was away at the farm. There was a lot of sorting-out to be done before it went on the market, so he didn't notice anything odd about me taking the opportunity to go into town to do some shopping.

Mr Pointer was waiting for me when I arrived at his office, and his round smiling face seemed even more cheerful than usual.

"Robin, good to see you. I've got some good news for a change. Come in and take a pew."

Things seemed to be looking up and I could feel my excitement rising.

"What news?"

"Cup of tea? I'll get Mrs Newstead to make us a pot before she leaves."

"Yes, yes, thank you. But what news?"

Settling back in his chair and tucking his thumbs into his waistcoat pockets – a favourite attitude of his – he continued: "I have had all the share prices checked up to the markets closing last night, and my guess is, and it's an educated guess," – he was spinning this out for full effect – "you will receive, after commission, of course, over £100,000!" He took his thumbs from his pockets, placed his arms on the desk and, leaning forward and looking me straight in the eyes, said, "What do think of that?"

I felt the blood draining from my face – unusual for me because it was usually the other way round.

"A hundred thousand pounds? But that is wonderful. James will not have to sell the Hall! Lady Ruth said it was there to be used, and if I can help James with it how she would have loved it. She knew something was going to happen. This is wonderful!"

The excitement was too much for me and my voice trailed off. As I was speaking, my eye had caught sight of a clump of arum lilies in the garden below the old man's office window.

He followed my gaze and said softly, "Lady Janney gave me those lilies. They were her favourites and she always wanted her friends to share her pleasures. You know, Robin, you should think carefully about how you handle this amount of money before you tell James." He was looking concerned as he continued: "James has made his decision about the estate and is able to enjoy his life more than he has for a long time. He knows that all his financial problems are over when he sells and that you will be able to travel and see some of the world without the worries attached to the estate. It has taken a large burden off his shoulders making this decision; but if you use this money to keep the Hall, you will both be tied to it and the money may soon drain away. Indeed it may very well swallow the money and both of you as well. You really must give this a lot of thought before telling James. He may well think it strange that his mother passed her shares to you." He paused a while before continuing: "She had a reason – a mother's reason – for arranging things as she did. She wanted to help her son, whom she loved dearly, and you, perhaps, are part of her reason. She loved you too. Who knows exactly what was in her mind, but things seem to be working towards what she had perhaps hoped."

All this took a little time to digest. What he said was true. James had made his decisions and was happier than he had been for a very long time. Now we had to face up to one more hurdle – his blood tests and transfusion next week.

"Yes, Mr Pointer, you are right. James has decided what he wants to do and there must be no going back. However, I would like you to complete the sale of the shares and put the money into a bank account for me. Then I shall know it is easily available if the estate fails to sell quickly and we need some ready cash to keep the place going."

"Rest assured, Robin, that I will do all that. Perhaps we can get together after James has been to hospital. Do, please, telephone me to let me know the results of the tests and, of course, when he comes out of hospital." He tidied the papers on his desk and rose to show me out of the office. "Goodbye, my boy."

When I arrived at the Hall, James was home and there seemed to be a completely changed atmosphere in the house. Even with the dark cloud of his illness still hanging over him, the fact that he had struck out on his own and taken the decision to dispose of the estate had so lightened his problems that he seemed like the young man – boy even – that I had first met.

He greeted me gaily. "I've prepared some tea on a tray in the drawing room. I didn't actually bake the cake – that would be too much to ask. Mrs Beeston – our old cook – called to see how I'm getting on, and she had baked a cake, bless her heart. I do miss the servants we had – not because we can't manage very well on our own, but because they had become such good friends."

I laughed and said, "Well, at least we know the cake will be good. I have doubts about the tea!"

The days passed in a dream and soon the day arrived for James's admission to hospital. We left early so that we would have time to go into the shopping area of the city to buy some silk pyjamas and a new dressing gown for James. The dressing gown he owned was not the sort to be worn in hospital and he never wore pyjamas. I laughed and joked on the way in that he was only trying to impress the nurses – or was it Paul? – with his silk pyjamas. He responded well, but I had the feeling he was only putting on a brave face for me.

How depressing hospitals are! So many worried people milling around, seemingly not knowing where they are supposed to be going or, if they do know, how to get there! Bewildering banks of signs point you in every direction, but the one you need seems to have been omitted.

We made our way to the reception desk and our gloom was soon lifted by a bright and breezy red-headed Irish girl who soon pointed us in the direction of our ward. I was dreading leaving him there, but hardly had the thought entered my head than James grabbed my shoulders, kissed me on the cheek and told me to go home. Looking over his shoulder as he hugged me, I could see the young redhead's eyes popping out of her head, but before I could get too embarrassed James had squeezed me and was on his way to the ward and I was on my way to the car.

James had made his farewells in his usual no-nonsense style. He obviously didn't want me to go to the ward with him, but in very positive style had told me to phone Paul the next morning to see when I could collect him.

How strange it seemed back at the Hall, and, after Bella's welcome, how quiet! I decided to give all the dogs a walk across the meadows, but no, James had always told me to feed them first and walk them second, then they would be happy until morning.

As I walked the meadows with the dogs, I pondered on how all this had happened. I was still so young and my world had changed completely. My parents would both have had heart attacks if they had known what was really happening and the amount of money that I had.

All my schoolmates with their girlfriends seemed a million miles away. There was certainly no one I could talk to on the subject. I could help Mum and Dad with some money, but how to explain where it had come from? Best wait until the Hall was sold, then I would concoct some sort of story to keep them happy. Mothers have a habit of sniffing out the truth, so I'd best be careful for a little while longer.

My mind was racing as fast as the dogs were chasing a rabbit across the water meadows. Perhaps I should get Mr Pointer to arrange the sale of the Hall to me anonymously and tell James that an overseas investor who was not coming back to England for ten years had bought it. We could say that he was quite willing for James to stay in the Hall for a reasonable rent and to act as custodian if he fancied the arrangement. That might just please James. He would be able to stay in the Hall and have the cash as well. Was I crazy? I thought it might just work. I decided to ring Mr Pointer in the morning. He would tell me if it was a good idea or not.

I hardly slept a wink that night with all the possibilities ringing in my head. It went through my mind that if James didn't want to stay he would still have the money and I would own the Hall. We would be able to live at Park Lodge and, without knowing it, he would, at some time in the future, have the opportunity to move back into the Hall. Meanwhile, I could let the Hall, perhaps to a wealthy young Arab who wanted to breed horses. That would make an interesting neighbour for us to entertain! On such flights of fancy, I whiled the night away.

Next morning, before my planned visit to see James in the afternoon, my excitement was so great that I rang Mr Pointer and told him all the things that had been going through my mind. I waited for what seemed an eternity for his reply, anticipating what I thought would be all his objections and reservations.

At last he spoke, and his first two words told me that all was well: "Yes, yes, Robin." And my heart leapt. "I think that that could work perfectly well. Then if at any time James feels he has done the wrong thing, and it causes him too much grief, you will still secretly own the estate and be able to move back in. Certainly, in my considered opinion, if you once sold the estate to an outsider you would never get it back again."

All the breath seemed to have left my body and I felt drained.

"Do you think you could put in an offer with the money you have raised from the portfolio? Then you can tell James all about the overseas investor and the possibility of his being able to stay on at the Hall if he wishes."

"Yes, yes, Robin, leave it all to me." I could hear the excitement in his voice.

"Let me know as soon as things start to move. I'm going to see James this afternoon and will call and let you know what the situation is."

"Please do, Robin. Goodbye."

I felt drained and could really have done with a stiff drink. There was no chance of that because I had to be ready to drive over to the hospital, but before that I had to speak to Paul.

"Hello, Paul. What news?" I was conscious that the excitement in my voice was not very appropriate, considering my reason for ringing.

"Hello, Robin. I'm sure you've been very worried, so I hope you managed to get some sleep last night. We have given James the transfusion and you will be able to pick him up after seven o'clock this evening. Of course he will have to come back in a few days' time for further checks."

"Thanks, Paul. Give James my love and tell him I'll be over just after seven. And thanks for everything."

I put the phone down, realising that I was still no clearer about James's condition. What a waiting game it all was!

When I arrived, James was waiting with his overnight bag in his hand.

"Hi," I said. "I hope you're not bringing those pyjamas home."

He laughed and gave me a huge hug.

"OK, I'll leave them for Matron," he replied, and with his arm over my shoulders we headed for the car.

The transfusion seemed to have had the same effect as two weeks' holiday in the sun.

Life at the Hall went on in a happy-go-lucky way. James was not aware of the secrets I shared with Mr Pointer. Why was the old boy as loyal to me as he was to the Janney family? Did he know something I didn't? After a few more days my curiosity got the better of me and I rang the solicitor.

"Don't worry, Robin – a few more days and I will ring James to make an appointment to come over to tell him about the overseas investor."

"Thank you, Mr Pointer. I owe you so much."

"Not to worry, Robin. All shall be well."

It was now high summer. How the time had flown! So much had happened and now there was just one more hurdle to get over – James's health. Why was I always thinking in terms of hurdles? Then I thought of course it was Father. He was always talking about hurdles – not the racing kind – it would never have occurred to him to put money on a horse or gamble in any way. Perhaps it came from a generation back – my grandfather, I had been told, was a shepherd in Yorkshire and they used hurdles to pen the sheep. Anyway, we were almost at the last hurdle because we were going, the next morning, to see Paul. James had been to see him a day or two before to have the blood samples taken and had heard that the results had come through.

Paul was waiting in reception when we arrived.

"Hello, you two. Come on in."

I could see no indication from his expression what his news was going to be.

"Take a seat."

His expression was more serious now and I thought that this must be like waiting for the arrival of the firing squad.

"James, I am sorry to have to tell you that the news is not good. Your condition, following the transfusion, was so good that I had hoped to be able to give you better news. However, the results of your latest tests show that the white-blood-cell count has increased again. I'm afraid we cannot do very much more except to put you on the course of treatment I have already mentioned. It will help to keep it in check, but you will have periods of extreme tiredness and weakness. You must try to keep away from infections of any kind – colds and that sort of thing. If things get really bad, we can increase the dosage, but I'm afraid the prognosis is not good. I'm sorry not to have better news for you."

I could see that Paul was genuinely upset, and I couldn't bring myself to say a word, so I just gripped James's hand and held it tightly.

James looked directly at Paul and said, "Tell me the truth: how much time are we talking about before things get really bad?"

"James, there is no telling. Provided you take things easy, eat and drink sensibly and keep clear of infection, you could have two, perhaps three, years. I'm sorry."

I could feel the colour draining from my face and watched it drain from James's. I gripped his hand even more tightly.

"Thank you for being so honest, Paul. We'd better get on with life and enjoy the time we have."

He stood and shook Paul's hand, and we left his office in silence.

The drive home was silent too. He insisted on driving and I gripped his knee as he drove. I felt an urgent need to be in close physical contact with him. It was as if, letting go of him, he might suddenly disappear and I might never see him again. I tried with all my strength to will him to know how much I loved him, but I couldn't bring myself to say one word in case I broke down. He needed all the strength that I could give him.

Back at home, James recovered something of his old self again, and I admired beyond words the strength that must have taken. We both got down on the floor when Bella came charging in from the kitchen. As we fondled the dog, the tears came; and as Bella raced away to find her ball, we held each other in the most powerful embrace.

The next morning we had a late breakfast. I reasoned that the only way to make James adjust to taking life in a more leisurely fashion was to set the pace myself. As the kitchen clock struck ten, the phone rang and James walked over and picked up the receiver.

"Hello, Mr Pointer," James said.

The old man must have been explaining to James all that I already knew but hadn't been able to mention, because it seemed to go on forever before James finally said, "Yes, later on in the week. Yes, go ahead and accept his offer. Thank you, Mr Pointer." And with that he hung up, walked back to the table and resumed his breakfast.

I waited for him to finish chewing his bacon for what seemed an eternity before he looked up, smiled and said, "Well, that all seems to be working out nicely."

I knew that he was teasing me, but I couldn't resist the temptation: "What's all working out? Tell me more," I demanded.

"Old Pointer has found an overseas investor looking for land with a good house attached. He has made an offer and Pointer is coming over later in the week."

"And?" I said.

'What do you mean, 'And?'

"What else?"

"Nothing else. I just told him to go ahead and accept the offer so that we could get on with the rest of our lives." And he returned to his breakfast.

Just what had Mr Pointer told James? Certainly not all that I expected.

"Well, that's good news." And I got up to make some more toast.

The next two days went like the wind. James busied himself deciding what we should take with us to Park Lodge. He'd decided that we might as well take what we liked, even if it meant getting rid of some of the furniture that was already there. The lodge was furnished rather sparsely for James's taste. He selected pictures and furniture, made lists and generally bustled about. I was pleased that his mind was occupied.

Friday found us once again in Pointer's office, and he told James that the offer was to include curtains and carpets and that his client was prepared to buy any of the larger furniture that might be surplus to James's requirements. I knew that much of it would be too large for the lodge – for example, the large settees that had been made for the drawing room and the dining-room table and chairs that sat sixteen. James was quite happy with all this. After all, the curtains and carpets couldn't have been changed for the last sixty years. They still looked perfect, but could never be moved. The farm was to include all the machinery – but there again, it was all so old that most of it would need replacing if the new owner was ever going to make a profit.

I was getting the occasional glance and smile from Mr Pointer. Nothing had been said as yet about James being able to stay on, but perhaps he was feeding him a bit at a time to see how he would adjust to it.

An hour later, with a glass of Mr Pointer's best Madeira under our belts, we took our leave.

James was profuse in his thanks for finding a buyer so quickly, but Pointer waved them aside, saying, "Not too difficult, my boy. There is an agency in London with a list of clients looking for this sort of property."

As we reached the office door, James turned and asked the question I had been dreading: "You haven't mentioned who the purchaser is?"

"There is a good reason for that, James. He has asked for the transaction to be handled using a proxy. His solicitors are in no doubt about his financial standing, and I too find this intriguing. He is familiar with both the estate and the Hall. I can only assume that he was either a friend or a business acquaintance of your father and has visited the estate at some time in the past."

"'Well, whoever it is, he's a godsend," said James, who didn't notice the wink that Mr Pointer aimed at me as we stepped out on to the pavement.

When we were back in the house, I suddenly realised how surprised I was at how well James seemed to be taking all that had happened. His spirits were consistently high, and he even jokingly said what a relief it would be "to leave all this rubbish behind". I had also noticed that he was drinking much less.

"I will tell Pointer that there are several things the new people can have at a price, such as the four-poster beds and the billiard table." And he was off once again with his lists and prices.

The following day, the lists were sent off to Mr Pointer via a village lady who worked as an office cleaner, and soon word came back that he was sure the new owner would be interested.

Later again, after receiving a call from Pointer, James replaced the receiver in an effervescent mood and reported, "That's another £5,000 for the odd bits of furniture!" And I was left wondering where all the extra money was coming from!

As we sat having coffee next morning, James came through to say that Mr Pointer would be over in about thirty minutes and asked me to keep an eye open for him.

"He has a couple of documents he wants me to sign. I just need to go down to the stables, but I should be back well before he arrives."

I kept a sharp lookout and, sure enough, about fifteen minutes later the old man's car came labouring round a bend up the drive and I waited for him on the gravel as he got rather stiffly out of his car.

"Good morning, Mr Pointer. James is down at the stables sorting out the old riding tack, so that gives us a minute or two to talk. What's happening? James has told me everything, I believe, but why haven't you told him about his being able to stay on?"

"I'm going to tell him this morning; but before we get into that, you should know that your shares came good and that is why I offered the extra for the furniture. It'll mean that you won't have a penny left except the rent coming in from Hall Farm and, of course, the rent we get from Park Farm once this has all been settled and a tenant has been found." He glanced over my shoulder and said rather sheepishly, "Good morning, James."

"Morning, Mr Pointer. I thought I heard your car on the drive. There's no mistaking the sound of that engine!" said James mischievously.

"Now, young man, no cheeky comments about my car! It's served me well for almost twenty-five years despite what people say."

"Only joking. You wouldn't be the same man arriving in a flashy new one, that's for sure. I've been down at the stables sorting out a few things. You wouldn't believe what gets stored away in fifty years. Come in – the coffee is bubbling."

As I poured the coffee, Mr Pointer said, "James, the overseas man who is buying your property has asked me to rent out the farm until he returns to England, and I thought that Nelson, who currently rents Hall Farm, might like to take it on."

"Oh! I thought Nelson bought the farm when I sold it." And he looked quizzically at Mr Pointer.

"My dear boy, you must remember that we sold it to an investment company and they asked me to find a tenant."

"I expect that I wasn't thinking too clearly at the time, but what does it matter? We've had the money and it helped for a time." And he shrugged his shoulders.

'Good old James,' I thought. 'Positive mental attitude!'

"Now here's the really interesting piece of news." Pointer leaned back and positioned his thumbs squarely in the pockets of his waistcoat. "The buyer is not coming back to this country for several years and he has said that he would be quite happy for you to stay on, if you wish, as a sort of custodian. He will pay all the maintenance costs and keep the place fully insured. He has said that if you are prepared to look after the place in a general sort of way – you know, the gardens and that sort of thing – then you can live here rent-free until his return. Naturally, he will give you plenty of notice when he wants to take up residence to give you time to move to Park Lodge. What do you say to that?"

Pointer and I both watched James for some sort of reaction, but it was several seconds before he looked up from his coffee cup and said, "I don't know. I've gotten quite used to the idea of moving to Park Lodge with Robin."

"My dear boy, you don't have to worry one little bit. Just take your time to make up your mind. He will have to find a caretaker to look after the house and gardens, or he might even let the house for a period. Just take your time."

Soon Pointer was off down the drive, grinding the gears as he went, and we were left alone together again. I had noticed that James had said nothing to Mr Pointer about the seriousness of his illness beyond a vague "Not too bad, thanks" when the old boy had enquired.

Summer passed by and we were still living in the Hall. James showed no signs of wanting to pack up for the move to Park Lodge, and I certainly didn't say anything to disturb the gentle rhythm of those lovely summer days. His medication had proved to be very effective, and we developed a routine of latish breakfasts, followed by walks with the dogs, a light lunch and a bit of gentle gardening. We had sorted and split up a lot of the perennials and moved them over to the new garden at the lodge. It was quite the wrong time of year to do that sort of thing, but they all seemed to be surviving and we kept them well watered. If it was wet, we would read or play snooker, and we swam every evening before supper and went early to bed.

Life went on like this until October, when James caught a very bad cold which quickly turned to a feverish influenza. Paul had become a very good friend, and with his partner (a male nurse called Jonathan) often came at the weekends to swim or dine with us. Daphne and the nephews had stayed for a short holiday in September, so it seemed the whole house rang with laughter.

Paul came more often as James got weaker, and Dr Foggarty called whenever his rounds took him past the gates. After a few anxious weeks, James was back in good spirits, but he was weaker than before. When I went to the garden he would watch from an old cane bath chair that he said, from its age, must have belonged to his great-great-grandparents!

Christmas came and the whole family came from Scotland: Simon, Daphne, Angus, Frazer and Frazer's girlfriend, a small Scottish lass with a loud voice and close-cropped hair. We had no help at the Hall except for Mrs Jones, a Welsh lady from the village, whom we quickly nicknamed Blodwyn, although I don't think she ever knew. She it was who hoovered and cleaned and polished all the extra rooms that were needed.

The boys were grown-up and refused to share, and Daphne certainly had no intention of allowing Frazer to share with his girlfriend – although, according to Blodwyn, her bed was rarely slept in!

I organised the food with the help of Angus. Being the same age, we got on very well together and seemed more like brothers. We soon banished everyone else from the kitchen and it all worked like clockwork.

The holidays were great fun and James was on his feet most of the time. James had told them of Paul's diagnosis and, although it went unspoken, I could tell that both Simon and Daphne felt that it might well be James's last Christmas. They did well to hide their great sadness under a cloak of gaiety. I had asked them to keep off the subject of how he was managing financially, and I had not told them about the sale of the Hall. James wanted it all to be kept secret until it was a fait accompli; he wanted no interference. I had heard some talk between them about the farm – James told them that he had let it to a local farmer. They all left after Hogmanay and we settled back into our old routine.

Dr Foggarty had arranged for a nurse to be available whenever James needed special care, and she was a great tonic for us both. Beryl was short, round, very muscular and had protruding teeth. She made me smile before she said a word. Her partner, Quentin – or 'lover', as she called him – was an artist and often came with her, bringing his oil paints and brushes. I often found him in the garden, painting the flowers and butterflies. He was great with James, never letting him get depressed, and I recall on one occasion hearing loud laughter coming from the drawing room and finding him painting James's portrait sitting at the grand piano. It is still a treasured possession.

Yet another birthday – my twentieth. Without my knowing it, James had organised Paul, Jonathan, Beryl and Quentin to bring food in and they gave me a splendid birthday supper. James had suggested that we should have scrambled eggs that evening in the kitchen. He had said, with a smile, that he didn't want me cooking on my birthday. But they all arrived and set up the table in the dining room and produced the most wonderful spread. James opened so many, many bottles of champagne that everyone got completely plastered and had to stay the night because no one was in a fit state to drive a car.

Spring slipped in and out and we were still at the Hall. James had said nothing about moving and I let it drift, happy in the knowledge that he was happy. I even phoned Mr Pointer one day to see if James had spoken to him about staying at the Hall; but no, he had heard nothing either. James would make his move when he was ready.

Just as summer arrived, James became very much weaker and Paul strengthened the dosage of his drugs. It was then that we decided to bring the Napoleonic bed – a great favourite of James – down to the drawing room and set it up beside the French windows, where he would have a wonderful view of the gardens and the countryside beyond. The Famous Five, as James called us – Paul, Jonathan, Beryl, Quentin and me – dismantled the bed and brought it, like a jigsaw puzzle, in many pieces, downstairs. Once it had been assembled and James was installed, he watched with much laughter as we reorganised the room, rehanging his favourite pictures so that he could see them clearly. Beryl left us for some time and returned with arms full of flowers which she had gathered from the garden. She filled vase after vase with them, filling the room with colour and fragrance.

Mr Nelson, who, as we hoped, had taken on the farm, had stocked up with a herd of Jersey cows. Spread as they now were across the meadows, they made the most perfect picture of all.

James, ensconced in his bed as we laboured, called for bottles of champagne to be opened, demanding that his bed be christened properly. My heart ached when I saw how bravely he managed to keep his good humour. He was much thinner now and I knew that Paul was very worried that he might be doing too much. I reassured him that, as far as James was concerned, laughter was the best medicine, and I think he saw the wisdom of that.

With the money from the sale of the Hall now safely in James's account, I was able to get Beryl to organise a – and I insisted 'good-looking' – male nurse who could be employed full-time. I was finding it more and more difficult, once she had left for the day, to keep the house in a tidy state and organise the cooking. Beryl, as always, came up trumps – another James, so we decided that, with two Jameses in the house, he would have to be called something else; and so it was that James II became 'Jimmy'. He was a great boost to us all for, as the summer days turned to autumn, James became much weaker and Jimmy's presence in the house at night was a great comfort. He rigged up a baby alarm between his room and James's, and that meant that I could get a good night's sleep so as to be on top form during the day. Jimmy had the most remarkable knack of being instantly wide awake if he heard the slightest noise. I spent most of the day just sitting quietly with James, reading to him if he wished, but nothing quite compares with the understanding silence between good friends.

What I had been dreading most came in late September. I had fallen asleep one afternoon on James's bed, holding his hand. When I woke up at four thirty his hand, still in mine, was as cold as ice. I knew immediately what had happened, but I could not move. I could hear Bella's gentle snores coming from the fireside across the room. I could feel the tears coming and the yawning cavern of loss that seemed to be opening before me. How was I going to manage without him? What must I do next?

I had heard the door open quietly, but had not looked up. Jimmy was there, and as I got shakily to my feet he put his arms around me, and a storm of sobs racked my body.

He let it subside a little and then said gently, "Take Bella and go for a walk, Robin. I will call Dr Foggarty and take care of anything else that needs to be done."

Thank God for Jimmy! He was a rock. I walked to the bed and looked sadly down at James and kissed him gently on the lips. Bella, sensing what had happened, whined quietly at my knees. I knelt down and hugged her and we left the room.

An Indian summer of unusual warmth and beauty blessed us. The parkland trees had assumed their autumn colours and the countryside was suffused with golden sunshine. The days drifted quietly by in such a haze that I could no longer separate in my mind one from another. Jimmy took care of everything. Simon, Daphne and the boys were coming to stay a few days before the funeral, which was a blessing because there were several things I had to give them. I knew about the will, but I don't think anybody else did.

Lady Veronica and Michael were coming to the funeral, but were staying at the King's Head Hotel in town, five miles from the Hall. I knew that they would stay on for the reading of the will. Mr Pointer had told me to explain to Daphne that he would read the will after refreshments had been served in the usual manner.

The funeral had been planned for eleven o'clock. I thanked heaven that the church was so close to the Hall because it meant that there was no need of cars before and after the service. Daphne had conveyed all the necessary information to Veronica by phone; James and I had not heard one word from her since the day after Lady Ruth's funeral, when James had inherited everything.

Mr Pointer had told me that I should follow James's coffin with Angus in support, as he was next in line for the title. I knew in my bones that this was not the best thing to do in the circumstances. Old Mr Pointer seemed tacitly to understand the relationship between James and me, but who else would? I can imagine the questions that would have flowed from all quarters – not least the villagers and those who had worked on the estate and were bound to be there. No, I would take a back seat, so to speak, and leave the family to lead.

Again Jimmy came up with the perfect solution.

"Look, Robin, why don't we act as bearers? Paul and Jonathan can join us, and I have already put the idea to Beryl's fiancé, Quentin, and she suggested her brother, Stephen, to make up the six. What do you think?"

"My God, Jimmy, that would solve everything. I shall be nearer to James and I shall be able to sit with you all rather than with the family. And there will be no awkward questions from Veronica. Nobody can possibly object because they all know that I have been James's companion for years and you have all been such a help to him during the last few months."

The day arrived, low mist cloaking the meadows, and I knew it would be sunny and warm. We all had breakfast together in the kitchen. Jimmy had stayed on although his nursing duties were over. He had such a natural air of authority that we all found ourselves following his instructions without even the least feeling of resentment. Daphne remarked over and over again how lucky we had been to find him to look after James.

Our close proximity to the church meant that we were able to wheel James's coffin on the nineteenth-century bier, which was kept in the church and had originally been used for James's great-great-grandfather's funeral. Jimmy and I collected it the day before and brought it over to the Hall and cleaned it thoroughly, greasing the axles for what must have been the first time for fifty years. It was then placed in the entrance hall ready to receive the coffin on the afternoon before the day of the funeral.

Jimmy had organised outside caterers to produce a light buffet, which had been set up in the billiard room to free the dining room for the reading of the will. The house seemed to be alive with people, and, as the clock struck ten, I left them to it and went to change. Many distant relatives had phoned to ask if they might park their cars in the stable yard. They knew we would be walking to and from the house if the weather held.

As I finished dressing, I saw a Rolls-Royce draw up beneath me at the front entrance. It was Veronica, of course – she wouldn't dream of using the stable yard. I was hoping that she would keep a low profile. I knew only too well how she liked to boss everybody about, and I didn't want her to upset Jimmy or any of the other willing helpers, who were unknown to her. As it was, she managed to surprise me again by not coming into the house at all, but she stood talking to several others who had gathered outside.

Jimmy and Paul had undertaken to move the bier from the house, and by the time I came downstairs it stood on the gravel path bedecked with the wild flowers we had picked from the estate the day before. We had arranged that Paul and I would walk alongside whilst the other four took the handle to guide it down the path to the church. I did not look back as we moved off, but I sensed that Angus and his brother were immediately behind, closely followed by family and friends.

As we walked through the park, it struck me how James would have loved all this. His beloved countryside was looking its best, the weather behaving properly, and his relations behaving in a civilised fashion for once. But as I thought of him and smiled, the tears began to form and I knew that for a while I must put all thoughts of him from my mind.

Behind me, I heard Jimmy say, "Are you OK?"

I couldn't turn to reply, so I felt in my pocket and half revealed James's silver hip flask, which I had filled with brandy.

"Ah, Dutch courage," I heard him mutter.

The vicar was waiting at the church porch as we arrived, and, having cast a smile over us, he took his place at the head of the bier and led us off into the silence of the church.

As we turned into the centre aisle, the organ music faded and he began to intone the wonderful words from the Book of Common Prayer: "I am the resurrection, and the life, saith the Lord. . . ."

The words were hypnotic, but my mind somehow managed to take in the sea of faces, half turned to watch the coffin pass, some familiar, some strange, and then on to the great window above the high altar, slanting sunlight pouring through the stained glass, transforming the white lilies to greens and reds.

"The Lord giveth and the Lord taketh away; blessed be the name of the Lord."

As the vicar announced the first hymn, we took our seats. We had chosen stirring hymns, and the first bars of 'Onward Christian Soldiers' brought the congregation to its feet and off to a good start. I had always had a strong dislike of hymns that nobody seemed to know and all feared to sing, but not today. There was a depth of feeling expressed in every word as each member of the congregation grieved personally for the young life they had all hoped so much of.

After some prayers and another hymn, it was Angus's turn. He had elected to read one of James's favourite poems:

Beyond the wheat and harvest of fruit upon the bough,
I recognise old autumn riding on the plough.
The year has passed its zenith and now it must decline,
Earth had its share of summer,
As I have had of mine,
As I have had of mine.

Another hymn, and I knew it was my turn. I had chosen an American Indian poem which David had introduced us to and which we had both come to love. I knew it was going to be difficult – no time for a sip of brandy – but Jimmy squeezed my hand as I got up. I realised that they were wet as I grasped the side of the lectern, but, partially hidden by the large brass pelican, I started on the poem that James had asked me to read if this day should ever arrive.

Do not stand at my grave and weep.
I am not there, I do not sleep.
I am a thousand winds that blow.
I am the diamond glint on snow.
I am the sunlight on ripened grain.
I am the gentle autumn rain.

When you wake in the morning hush,
I am the swift, uplifting rush
Of quiet birds in circling flight.
I am the soft starlight at night.

Do not stand at my grave and weep.
I am not there, I do not sleep.

There was complete silence in the church as I read; and when I reached the line about the stars, my mind flew back to the days of my North Star and my eyes filled with tears. That was where it had all started.

I needn't have worried. As I walked back to my seat, it seemed that most of the congregation had handkerchiefs to their faces.

The vicar brought us all back to this world as he introduced Simon, who gave the eulogy. He spoke movingly about James, describing his days at school and university. It was through their friendship that he had met Daphne. I realised that Simon had probably known James better than anyone and was certainly aware of our relationship, although he had never, in the slightest degree, revealed that knowledge.

Before leading us out to the churchyard for the interment, the vicar announced that everybody would be welcome to come back to the Hall for refreshments; and as we moved James's coffin back through the nave, the congregation sang 'Praise My Soul the King of Heaven' with great gusto.

As we stood at the graveside, I recalled how little time it seemed since we had laid James's father and mother in the family plot and how my life had changed in the years that followed. As his final tribute, Frazer had asked to read from a book by Henry Scott-Holland, who, I learned later, was a canon of St Paul's and a distant relative of James.

Frazer read quietly:

Death is nothing at all. It does not count.
I have only slipped away into the next room.
Nothing has happened.

Everything remains exactly as it was.
I am I and you are you,
And the old life that we lived so fondly together is untouched, unchanged.
Whatever we were to each other, that we are still.

Call me by the old familiar name.
Speak to me in the easy way which you always used.
Put no difference into your tone.
Wear no forced air of solemnity or sorrow.

Laugh as we always laughed at the little jokes that we enjoyed
  together.
Pray, smile, think of me, pray for me.
Let my name be ever the household word that it always was.
Let it be spoken without an effort, without the ghost of a shadow
  upon it.

Life means all that it ever meant.
It is the same as it ever was.
There is absolute and unbroken continuity.
What is this death but a negligible accident?

Why should I be out of mind because I am out of sight?
I am but waiting for you, for an interval,
Somewhere very near, just round the corner.

All is well. . . .

With that, he closed the book, and I could see the tears running
from sad eyes. I knew that both Angus and Frazer had loved James
dearly and that they had so enjoyed their time with him at the Hall.
Now it was all gone. I wondered if it had crossed their minds that
the estate might be coming to them. Had their parents mentioned
the possibility to them? I knew that the next few hours were going
to be very difficult for me.

Frazer walked over to me and said, "Robin, this is for you.
I picked it up at Hatchards' when I was in London. I knew that
James loved this passage – as he loved you. I am so sorry."

With that he was gone before I could thank him. Had I been
selfish? I knew I was going to have trouble this day, but, of course,
so was everybody else who had been close to James.

I decided to take the longer route back to the Hall, and Jimmy, who had been watching from the church porch, tagged along.

"Would you like some company or would you rather be alone?" he asked.

"Thanks. I'm taking the long way home. I want to get back to the Hall after all the family have got there. If they are all deep in conversation, they might not notice my arrival and I won't have to get too involved."

As I spoke, I was startled to see, just behind him, an exact replica of himself.

Jimmy noticed the surprise on my face because he half turned and said, "Sorry, Robin, this is my brother, Barry – well, actually my younger twin." And he grinned shyly.

"Hello, Barry. Thank you for coming over." And we shook hands.

"Pleased to meet you, Robin. I told Jimmy I would come over in case he wanted to leave after the funeral. I said I would collect him and all his rubbish."

"Rubbish! You call my wardrobe rubbish after what I see you wearing most of the time?"

"Yes, I know just how many rags you cart about," he said sarcastically.

"Don't take any notice of him, Robin. He's terribly spoilt, being the baby of the family."

I could not get over just how much alike they looked – except that Barry had much shorter hair.

"Both of you can stay. There is no need to hurry away this evening. Daphne and the boys are staying until the morning, so you can help me out with some moral support. I feel that I'm going to need it after they've heard the will. Just make yourselves at home; Jimmy can show you the room next to his own. I'm afraid you will have to share a bathroom as it's between the two rooms."

Barry said, "Let Robin get away whilst we go and join the throng before they finish all the food." And with that they were off.

I ambled across the two water meadows which connected the footpath to the south side of the Hall. As I got to the stile I sat down to think. What was going to happen next? I was so young and I had all this on my hands. Mr Pointer would know how to handle things. I had caught his eye a couple of times during the funeral service and he had smiled sympathetically across the aisle. It was comforting to feel him so close; I knew he was grieving very badly because he had loved James so much. He was always trying to father us when we had meetings or he came to join us for a meal. I think, perhaps, that he had told Lady Ruth that he would keep an eye on us both till we had 'grown up'. I thought I would get him to sell it all. I had Park Lodge, so the money could be invested, and then I could think about the future. James had said that he would leave me a few things, so I would be able to furnish the lodge as I wanted it. I wanted to keep some of the portraits of the family so that they would be there for the boys when I had finished with the house. I decided to hang the one of Lady Ruth in the sitting room and the one of James that Quentin had painted, just before he died, in my bedroom. It was a good likeness, although Quentin had given him a tan so that he didn't look so ill. It showed him as I had always known him, dark and tanned – he had spent so much time in the gardens or about the farms.

As the tears came with the thoughts of him, I remembered the flask in my coat pocket and downed it all with a few quick gulps. The burning sensation brought me back to reality with a jerk. For my entire liking for good wines, which James had taught me, I had never really taken to brandy. The taste still took my breath away – perhaps it was too much at one go!

He would say, "Just a little at a time and swill it around your mouth before swallowing."

We sometimes used to get very tight just trying out all the different liqueurs on those dark winter evenings, on several of which we didn't even get to bed, but slept on the fireside rug with Bella.

'Enough!' I thought. 'I had better get back to the Hall.'

As I approached, some people were already leaving. Most of them were former estate workers and other villagers and I expect that they had had a few glasses of champagne and a plateful of smoked salmon. They were so like myself a few years before, wanting to try all these exotic foods – now it was their turn for a taste of the good life.

"Robin, I was getting worried about you." It was Mr Pointer, looking very concerned.

"No need to have worried. I walked back by the water meadows and" – pulling the empty flask from my pocket – "getting a little Dutch courage on the way!"

"Not too much, I hope," he said, smiling.

"No, just enough to keep me going until bedtime."

"Fine. I'll tell you when I am ready to read the will. Most people seem to have finished eating, so in about half an hour I'll get the family together in the dining room. It was a splendid idea of yours to set up the food in the billiard room – I could spread out my papers so much more comfortably on the dining-room table. I took the liberty of asking Jimmy to place both water and champagne on the table. I've the feeling that some of them may need reviving after the will has been read." And he chuckled as he bustled off.

I wandered through the entrance hall, saying "Hello" and "Thank you for coming" to the people that I knew, or who knew of me. I rather hoped that James's sisters had thanked family and close family friends. I felt that it was hardly my place to do so, and it would have seemed strange to them as I hadn't even been introduced to most of them. Some of them knew that Lady Ruth had left me the use of Park Lodge, which explained my continued presence on the estate.

My wandering took me into the kitchen and there they all were – Paul, Jonathan, Beryl, Quentin, Jimmy and Barry – sitting at the great pine table, in the centre of which languished two chicken carcases, largely stripped of their flesh.

"My God, it looks like a scene from *The Private Life of Henry VIII*. I hope you've left some for me!"

"There's another one in the fridge. I cooked them last night knowing full well that we would all need something more substantial than canapés," said Jimmy, laughing, his face covered with grease from ear to ear.

So I sat down and tucked into the remaining chicken. The mood had changed now – the solemnity had passed to be replaced by stories of James's funny doings and how he had made us laugh so much. I let the laughter sink into me, knowing that in a very short time I would be faced with another change of mood and – fireworks! As I tucked in, using my fingers, Mr Pointer wandered through the kitchen door.

"I guessed you were all in here, and it all seems to be going very well out there." And he gestured towards the billiard room.

"Yes," I replied.

I thought that James's sisters were getting very quickly into organising the Hall. I hoped they wouldn't get too used to it!

"Robin, I think that it's about time I brought all this to a close. I'll call the family to the dining room. Give me five minutes and then join me there. Oh, and by the way, I shall need Paul and Beryl there as well."

As I rinsed my greasy fingers at the sink, I saw Paul and Beryl exchange quizzical glances.

"Let's go and polish them off," I shouted.

The champagne we had consumed with the chicken had had its effect, and that, coupled with the flask of brandy earlier, had raised my courage to about as high as it was likely to get in the circumstances.

When we arrived at the dining room, I could see that Mr Pointer had got the family seated towards one end of the table, leaving some empty chairs together at the other.

"Do come in and take a seat, Robin. Yes, please, you too, Paul and Beryl. I have had a word with the caterers and they are tidying up under Jimmy's expert supervision."

As the three of us took our seats, my thoughts turned to Barry. I still had not got over how much he resembled Jimmy, but there was something else – closeness. I had a strange feeling that we were to become very close friends. Somehow he just seemed to belong.

Mr Pointer coughed slightly and opened his briefcase. As he did so, the noise at the table quietened.

"As you know, I have been the family solicitor for many, many years."

There were smiles on most of the faces around the table, but not Veronica's.

He continued: "James asked me to draw up his will in February, knowing that he had only a few months to live. He was anxious that everything should be settled before his illness made it too difficult for him." He paused, took a deep breath and announced, "This is the last will and testament of Lord James Alfred Janney: 'I leave to my sister, Veronica, my mother's set of sapphire jewellery. To Daphne, my mother's set of rubies. . . .'"

I knew that these had been left to James to pass, should he ever marry, to his wife.

Mr Pointer hesitated for a few seconds, noticing that Veronica had engaged Daphne in rather animated conversation. I knew exactly what she would be saying because there had been another set of jewels – diamonds – which James had shown me. I didn't know what James had done with them – he might very well have sold them in the difficult times. He had said nothing to me, but I knew how many times there had been when the money would have proved of more use than the stones.

Another cough came from the old solicitor and he continued: "'I leave to my nephews, Angus and Frazer, the sum of £20,000 each to be held in trust until their twenty-fifth birthdays. . . .'"

Another buzz of conversation between the sisters. They obviously knew nothing about the sale of the estate.

"'To Dr Paul Hampton and Miss Beryl Tinesdale I bequeath the sum of £2,000 each as a mark of my appreciation of their professional help and their wonderful kindness. . . .'" There followed a few minor bequests to the local doctor and some former estate workers and then, looking pointedly at me: "'To Robin, I leave the remainder of my monies and my goods and chattels.'" Mr Pointer looked up and surveyed the astonished faces around him. "That concludes the reading of Lord James's will."

Veronica leapt to her feet, sending her chair flying backwards into the wainscot.

"Mr Pointer, there must be some mistake. What about the Hall and estate? Who has inherited that?" She was fuming.

"I am sorry, Lady Veronica – didn't Lord James inform you that he had sold it when he had great cash problems following the outbreak of foot-and-mouth disease?"

"Sold! Sold! Why didn't anybody inform us? It was ours as well."

She looked over at Daphne for support as she collapsed into the chair that Angus had replaced behind her, but it was Simon who spoke: "I knew that he had financial problems because we spoke about it once. He would not hear of borrowing money because he felt that he might not be able to repay it."

He placed his arm around Daphne's shoulder – she was weeping.

Veronica was now in a frenzy.

"But why weren't we told? We could have bought it. Simon, you could have bought it for the boys. Mr Pointer, why did you not tell us?" And she glared at the old man.

"Lady Veronica, it was Lord James's wish that the estate be sold, and that is what I did. It was sold to an investor who did not wish to occupy the Hall for some years and he told Lord James he could stay as long as he wished. All expenses were paid by the new owner from the farms, which are rented out. Lord James was thus able to clear all his debts and overdrafts, and I am happy to say he had no more worries about the spectre of bankruptcy." He paused and in measured tones continued: "Do remember, Lady Veronica, that Lord James was very ill. Perhaps if you had visited him, he might have seized the opportunity to tell you." He snapped his briefcase shut, and with great dignity walked from the dining room saying, over his shoulder, "Robin, will you walk with me in the garden? I need to speak to you privately and I have something to hand over to you."

Smiling, I nodded, and as we left the dining room I heard Veronica's high-pitched voice and the words 'disgusting' and 'diamonds'.

As we walked back through the house to the front entrance, I noticed how quiet and empty it all seemed. Everybody had left – even the caterers. I only hoped that Jimmy and the rest were still there, but I couldn't see any signs that they were still in the house. However, as we entered the walled garden we met Jimmy and Barry.

"I'm so glad you are still here. Have the others left?"

"Yes, they asked me to tell you that they will telephone you tomorrow. Paul said you were to take his professional advice and get an early night. Barry and I will take up your invitation and stay the night – I'll get you a light supper later on."

"That's great. We can eat together in the kitchen." And I gave Jimmy a hug. "You know, you've both been wonderful – you all have. I don't know that I could have managed these last few days without you."

"It's what friends are for," said Barry as they walked on.

"Mr Pointer, can you tell me how much money there is left in James's account? Jimmy has been so good to James – and to me, too – that I think he should be treated in the same way as Paul and Beryl. I know he has been paid a salary, but all that he did went far beyond the call of duty."

The old man looked directly at me as he said, "You have the right instincts, my boy. I intended to talk to you about that. James mentioned the possibility to me on one occasion, but then, what with his illness, it must have gone from both our minds. Don't worry – I know there has been a lot of expense, but if we give Jimmy the same as the other two, and with all the taxes and other commitments out of the way, you should have about £10,000 left. There is also, of course, the rental income from the farms."

"No, I'm not worried, Mr Pointer, because when all this is over I cannot see me staying on here."

"Robin, if you'll take my advice – for what it's worth – you'll take your time before making any decisions. Leave it until next summer. All your love and most of your memories are here, and I am but a phone call away if you need help or advice."

"I feel sometimes that I am too young to have so many memories. I only really loved everything here because of my love for James. I can't imagine that things will ever feel the same again, but I'll take your advice, as always, and leave it all until next year. Winter is coming and I really don't feel like doing anything at present."

"Well, I'm glad to hear it. Now, James asked me to hand this to you if anything happened to him." And he passed me a large brown envelope. "Go and read it quietly and alone. I shall see you in the next few days."

Mr Pointer turned to walk back to his car and I moved towards the greenhouse. I could feel the tears coming as I opened the package.

> *Dearest Robin,*
>
> *I know you loved me, and I hope with all my heart that you realise how much I love you.*
>
> *It was so strange, but I knew from the very first moment we met that this was going to happen. Something seemed to flow between us.*
>
> *Thank you for all the love you gave my mother and for every single second you gave to me. I so looked forward to many years together, to sharing all the things we had both come to love so much: the house, the gardens, and oh, the champagne! But it was not to be.*
>
> *I do hope that, someday soon, you will find someone else to love. You have so much to give and share.*
>
> *I know that in a lot of people's eyes our love was wrong, but can anything that is truly loving and selfless be wrong? Robin, in case you should change as you get older, and fall in love with a girl, I leave you my mother's diamonds. Mr Pointer has them in safekeeping, so just ask him. They are for you to do with as you wish. I think Mother would be pleased – she loved you dearly, almost like another son. Would you also wear the gold signet ring that she gave me on my twenty-first birthday and – think of me?*
>
> *I shall always be looking over you, and you will be with me forever.*
>
> *James*

As I finished reading his letter, I had arrived at our favourite spot in the garden – the greenhouses – and then the tears flowed as they had not done for days. Blinded, I looked back to where Mr Pointer had been, but he had gone and I was completely alone.

I moved into the warmth of the greenhouses and was almost overwhelmed by the scent of the arum lilies. We had picked most of them to cover James's coffin and decorate the church, but some remained and their perfume seemed to trigger the great bursts of sobbing that racked my body as I sank to the ground with my back against the old potting bench. I thought that my heart must break.

Some thirty minutes – perhaps more – must have passed before I felt able to walk back to the Hall. When I did so, it was to find Daphne and Simon loading their car. Strange – I thought they had intended to stay overnight.

Suddenly, I heard the gravel of the path scattering in all directions, and from behind me came cries of "Robin, Robin, we've been looking all over the place for you."

I turned to find the two boys catching up from the direction I had come from. Perhaps they had looked into the greenhouses and not seen me sitting on the floor.

"We are so sorry, but Mother is so upset she wants to leave tonight. I think Auntie Veronica has upset her. She did not stop saying awful things about you till she left ten minutes ago. Mr Pointer told her to follow him into town so that she could collect her mother's jewels and take them with her."

All this from Angus, but now Frazer joined in: "Mr Pointer told us you were staying on here at the Hall. Can we come and stay with you in the holidays?"

Like me, he always blushed when asking favours!

"Yes, of course, any time you like. Just telephone and get on the train. I can always fetch you from the railway station. Listen – I mean it, whenever you like – and your parents."

"I don't think they will ever come back."

"I'm sorry. I thought they liked me. Never mind." And I gave them both a hug and they sped off to the car.

As I approached, Daphne was already in the front seat, but Simon came over and before he could speak I said, "I'm sorry you're leaving so soon. I had hoped you would all be staying overnight."

"That damned Veronica. She has upset everybody with her tongue. Daphne is in a real state. I am sorry, Robin, but if you ever want to talk, you have my telephone number. I think the boys wanted to ask you."

"Yes," I said, cutting him off before he could finish, "and I've told them they can come and stay whenever they like. And that goes for you and Daphne too."

"We'll have to see about that. She's so upset about losing James and the estate too. I think she felt it was going to Angus."

He opened the car door and got in.

"What will be . . ." I said as I closed the door for him and they moved off down the drive.

Things were looking up. I had forgotten about them staying, but now there would be only Jimmy and his brother and we could relax a little. God knows we needed to! Time for a cup of tea, but where was Bella? She had been hiding all day, sensing that something was wrong.

The evening was so peaceful and quiet.

We had supper in the kitchen and, when we had finished eating and washed up, Jimmy said, "May I show Barry round the house? He has only seen the gardens."

"Yes, give him the half-crown tour. Take a glass of champagne with you, and while you're about it just check there's nobody left from this afternoon and that all the windows are locked. I shall be all right tonight with the pair of you here, but tomorrow night is going to be very strange being on my own."

With that said, they topped up their champagne and left Bella and me alone.

"Well, old girl, we've got all this to look after for a while, so you had better become a guard dog."

She sidled up to me and I gave her a hug – the only one left to hug, I thought sadly.

Next morning, I asked if they would both like to stay on for a while, but Jimmy said that his ex-girlfriend had phoned him the day before to say that she had heard about James and thought that Jimmy might be looking for a new nursing job. She was currently caring for an elderly colonel and his wife in Gloucestershire. The old man had recently developed Parkinson's disease, so more help was needed. She'd told Jimmy that it was a lovely Georgian house and that his quarters would be very comfortable. On top of all that, the salary was very generous. In short, he had accepted the offer.

He must have seen the look of disappointment on my face because he said, "Robin, it would be wonderful to stay on, but my presence holds too many memories for you. You must get used to managing without me, and, in any case, I am a nurse and I must do my own thing."

I looked across at Barry.

He smiled and said, "Well, I am between jobs – nothing on at all. If you like, I will keep you company. I could do some gardening and anything else you have in mind. I come pretty cheap as long as there is plenty of good food and wine."

I grinned, and said, "Fine – that's settled. You can have Jimmy's room. It's much nicer than the one you are in at the moment and you can stay as long as you want."

The weeks leading up to Christmas found us very busy. We cleaned and sorted out all the drawers in every piece of furniture. We cleaned everywhere and moved things around and polished every piece of silver and gradually brought a sparkle to every room. A lot of routine jobs had been neglected during James's illness; we deliberately had no help because we wanted the place to ourselves. Now it was good to see the old house back as it was when Lady Ruth was alive. She always kept a tight ship – everything in its place and spick and span.

Christmas arrived once more and Barry and I were going to be on our own. I had invited Mum and Dad to come for lunch, but they said they would be happier in their own home. I told them that we would come home for lunch and they could meet Barry.

The boys, Angus and Frazer, were coming to stay for the first week in January before going back to university.

The four of us had a week of great fun: from walking to swimming, billiards, cards and drinking. It was the most relaxed week I had had for months, and it was then that I began to realise that I was becoming very fond of Barry. He seemed always to have been around, and it seemed quite natural for us to be together. Just before Christmas he moved into the bedroom next to mine.

Our closeness had developed slowly without either of us realising the extent to which we had become attached to each other. It just seemed we were on the same wavelength from the first time we met.

Mr Pointer came over quite regularly, and he had taken a great shine to Barry. He could see that he was a great help to me and seemed to sense that our relationship had moved on to a different footing. He was always on hand if I needed advice: him never pressing, and me never refusing. The old man knew too much about the estate for me to ignore what he had to say.

One day, I suddenly found myself saying to him, "Mr Pointer, I don't think we will stay here much longer. I don't think this lifestyle is really for us. We ought to be working at something more productive. Like James, I find that there are lots of worries that I could very well do without. We could live in Park Lodge and find something else to do – perhaps a small restaurant – which would be fun."

He heard me out, listening patiently to all my reasons for selling the estate, and finally said, "Robin, wait until spring, until after your birthday. You'll be twenty-one and nobody will be able to argue." And he smiled that knowing smile of his.

"Yes, Mr Pointer," I replied, knowing that I was putting things off again and not feeling unduly worried.

"You know you have the rents coming in from both the farms, and your bank balance is gradually increasing. As long as you have no large expenses, you won't need to worry too much. In fact, if the financial situation keeps improving as it has, you will be able to afford some help in the house and a gardener too."

"OK, Mr Pointer, you're the boss. I'll leave things until after the 14th of February – but no longer. Then some decisions will have to be made."

"Oh, I think you will find things are considerably clearer then," he said, and he gave me that knowing glance of his.

My birthday arrived and Barry had arranged a party. All our old friends – Paul, Jonathan, Beryl and Quentin. Jimmy arrived with the ex-girlfriend, Tammy, who was now his girlfriend again. He had settled down in Gloucestershire in what he described as 'the most beautiful house' with an equally delightful old couple. Their niece and her boyfriend had agreed to stay for a few days to enable Jimmy to escape for my birthday celebrations.

Mr Pointer joined in and had a jolly time. We never ever got round to asking him what his first name was. Barry joked that he had been christened 'Mr Pointer'. It was several years later, when he died, that we found out that it was Cuthbert. By then, most of his clients had died. As he grew older, he refused to take new ones on and I think by then we were one of a very few left.

We also asked several of the people who had helped on the estate over the past few years. Most of the estate workers who had become friends when James was alive had got jobs on the farms when the new tenants had taken over. This had been a great relief to James as most of them had worked for his father and he couldn't bear the thought of asking them to leave.

We had a wonderful evening, and we opened yet more of the champagne that James had put down. Looking around the cellar when we fetched the bottles, I realised that the racks were nearly empty again. A few bottles of port and brandy were beginning to get a respectable sprinkling of dust, and I recalled with a tear how James had restocked the racks as soon as he received the money for the Hall – most of them with champagne!

After Lady Ruth died, the cellar had gradually been emptied. There was never enough money to restock.

James always said, "Robin, the racks should always be full. Always buy more and put them down as you drink it."

He always took me down there in the early days of our relationship, when the family were around the Hall. It was one of the few places we could make love – down among the bottles! It was a special place to me – so many memories.

At the end of the evening, when we were all gathered in the entrance hall saying our goodbyes, everybody remarked how good it was to see the old place come back to life again and how much James would have loved to be there.

Mr Pointer said his goodbyes and said he would pop over in the next week.

"Yes, come over for lunch on Friday."

"Splendid, splendid. See you at noon on Friday."

What did Mr Pointer want now? He had a twinkle in his eye. Perhaps I was imagining things and it was only the champagne. He tottered down the front steps and into the waiting taxi.

As we were going upstairs to bed, I said to Barry, "I don't know what old Pointer has got to tell me, but he was in a very excited state when he left. He's got something up his sleeve."

"Well, you're just going to have to sleep on it and wait until Friday morning," said Barry, and he yawned.

"Why don't you stay in my bedroom tonight?"

"Too much champagne," he said.

On Friday morning, snow had fallen overnight and the park was looking very festive. We never seemed to get any at Christmas, but some nearly always fell in February. How good it looked before footprints and tyre tracks spoiled it all! When I opened the front doors and looked out over the meadows there was an air of muffled stillness that was almost unearthly.

Mr Pointer soon put an end to that! Precisely at noon his car came racketing up the drive. He must have set off very early to get there on time. He never seemed to do more than twenty miles an hour, and yet I never knew him to be one minute late – or, indeed, much more than one minute early – in all those years. In the course of the sixty or so years that he had been coming to the Hall he must have got his driving time sorted out for just about every conceivable set of driving conditions. I know he was the bane of every tractor driver in the county because of the snail's pace at which he drove that old car.

I opened the front doors and Bella bounded out, giving him a warm welcome and covering him in an avalanche of snow.

"Now, Bella, don't jump up – you will get into trouble with your master. Good morning, Robin. What a splendid sight!" he said, looking over the parkland.

"Yes, it's wonderful when the snow is fresh. Look at the oak trees. Aren't they fantastic with the snow on them?"

"That's how I love to see them. They would make a wonderful Christmas card if you took a photograph of them."

"I know, but I always leave it too late. By the time I remember, it's been spoiled by traffic and we don't get any more. Never mind – I'll get it right one day. Come on in. The cork is pulled and we have a roaring fire in the drawing room."

The old man shrugged off his coat and bustled into the warmth of the drawing room, where Barry had already poured a couple of glasses of wine, and we sat down by the fire.

After a few minutes, and with the glasses half empty, Mr Pointer said softly, "Robin, I have something rather special to tell you." I could tell by his manner that this was something more serious than I had anticipated.

Barry said, "Ought I to leave you two alone?"

"I think, Barry, that, in the circumstances, it might be better if you did," said Mr Pointer and, seeing the look of amazement on my face, he continued: "Robin, you will understand why I have asked Barry to leave in a minute or two. You can decide later whether to tell Barry or not. That is for you to decide."

Barry got to his feet and said, "Don't worry, Robin – I quite understand what Mr Pointer is asking and I'm very happy about it. I'll go and set the lunch table." And he left the room.

"Very well, then. I have to tell you that you have, on your twenty-first birthday, come into an inheritance of some £20,000." My bemused expression prompted him to continue: "When you were born, Lord Cameron set up a trust fund in your name which has grown considerably over the years. What I have to say next will come as a shock to you. When your mother was working at the Hall, she and Lord Cameron fell in love and you were the consequence. Of course, it was a difficult situation. Lord Cameron was already married and it was fortunate that, being the good man that he is, the man you have always known as Father has always thought you were his son. They had been childhood sweethearts and he was very much in love with your mother. You owe him a great deal. I don't know if your mother ever told him.

"Lord Cameron was also quite emphatic that you were not to be told until you were twenty-one unless your mother decided herself that the time was right before that date. I have to say that your mother and your father would never take any money from His

126

Lordship, but he did insist that she accept a very valuable silver claret jug. It was given so that if at any time she needed money quickly she could sell it. I expect you have seen it. The Norfolk Regiment presented it to Lord Cameron's grandfather – your great-grandfather – in 1895."

"Yes," I said, still in a state of shock, "I have seen it in the china cabinet, but I have never seen what is written on it because the cabinet is always locked and the inscription was always turned to the wall." It was at that moment that the full implication of what I had been told hit me with physical force. "So James was my half-brother."

There was complete silence in the room apart from the crackling and occasional minor explosion from the log fire. Mr Pointer put his glass on the table and came round to put his arm around my shoulders.

"Yes, but you loved each other. There is no shame in that; neither should you feel any." And then, with a sigh: "It is given to very few of us to experience the kind of love you shared with James. It will always be with you, and I would not wish you to feel anything other than pride."

I knew in my heart that the old man was regretting his own lack of such a love, and my eyes filled with tears.

"Lady Ruth knew a lot more than her family gave her credit for. I know she was worried about the possibility of her daughters turning you out if James got worse and couldn't cope with the estate. She knew that James was not as he should be – mothers know everything. Do you mind if I help myself?" he asked, picking up the decanter.

"Help yourself, and top me up, please."

We sat in silence for about ten minutes more, sipping our brandies. I could feel the warmth of it spreading through me, giving a pleasantly mellow feeling in the pit of my stomach, which made me realise that I was getting hungry. No sooner had the thought crossed my mind than there was a knock on the door and Barry appeared.

"Lunch will be ready in ten minutes in the dining room." And then he took in our faces and a look of astonishment came over his own. "You both look as if you've seen a ghost," he said, paling visibly.

"Yes, one just wafted through before you came in," I joked, hoping to set his mind at rest. "Can you manage?"

I knew perfectly well that he could manage whatever needed to be done, and I also knew that such a question made him furious. He wagged his head and raised his eyebrows at Mr Pointer and was gone.

"We've got ten minutes to get ourselves prepared for lunch. I'll just tell Barry that we've had a few words about the estate and I got a bit upset, but that now all is well. I'll think a bit more before telling him the truth of the matter. Now, let's go and see what he has cooked."

I knew already what we were having for lunch; and although Mr Pointer liked to express surprise when the food arrived at the table, I knew that he did too. The brandy would have had to cripple his sense of smell for him not to be able to recognise the odour of game casserole drifting through from the kitchen.

How we enjoyed the game through the winter months! I had kept the shooting rights over the two farms, so on many occasions we would walk across the meadows with Bella and shoot only what we needed to eat. Barry had decided that he didn't want to learn to shoot. Being a city boy, he had no interest in the sporting side of the estate, but he loved the gardens and would often help the tenant farmer with his animals.

Somehow the stimulation of our conversation had made both the old solicitor and me so hungry that we tucked into the food with great gusto. Poor Bella's face, down at my knee, was a picture of anticipation. She had always been fed what was left over from the table and was obviously giving up hope that anything was coming her way today. She would eat anything, from bones to apple crumble – it was all grist to her mill.

The three of us had a lively conversation and I could see that Barry was searching for some indication of what we had been talking about which appeared to have upset me so much. Mr Pointer, however, steered the conversation adroitly around to the management of the house and gardens. We had no worries about the farms. The rents had been set at a very reasonable rate on full repairing leases, so we didn't have to worry about keeping the barns, cowsheds and so on in good order. What outgoings there were, largely related to the house and its outbuildings and, as the main roof had recently been completely refurbished, it was mainly a question of keeping the paintwork up on the windows and so on. Barry and I had recently started to work on the restoration of the glasshouses, but for me that was a labour of love.

The parkland was rented out to one of the tenant farmers for his cattle and sheep. It always looked far nicer with animals grazing across it, and the grass was kept short and in good fettle.

Barry and I had got the kitchen gardens into shape and were producing nearly everything we needed. He had found a shop in town run by a long-haired hippy and his girlfriend, who took all the surplus vegetables; Barry bartered them for flour, bread and sugar and all the other dry goods we needed for our own use. Our living costs, therefore, were kept to an absolute minimum. Mr Pointer said that it all sounded like a return to merry England, and the wine we had consumed made us laugh louder than his feeble joke really deserved. By the time we had consumed the apple crumble we had convinced ourselves that we were doing very well indeed – and, frankly, I think we were.

I still had the nagging feeling that I would not continue to live there happily. I seemed to have this feeling about moving on continually at the back of my mind.

Everything seemed to remind me of James, whom I still loved dearly, and I knew that if things were to develop with Barry, and we were very close, it wouldn't work out if we were there.

By the time we had shoehorned Mr Pointer into his old car, and he had gone racketing down the drive, I could see that Barry could hardly contain his curiosity.

As soon as the car had wheezed and grunted its way round the bend, he grabbed me from behind and said, "Now, what have you two been plotting?"

"Nothing much. We had a disagreement about the estate. I told him I wanted to sell and move on."

"What do you mean, sell and move on? I thought that you were just living here, just looking after it for a few years until the person who owned it returned from abroad. I thought I had lost the thread of the conversation in the dining room when you were talking about the maintenance of the house, knowing that it belonged to somebody else. You both seemed to know what you were talking about, despite the amount of wine you had drunk. I just hope we don't find the old boy in the rhododendrons tomorrow morning."

I laughed and said, "That car can find its own way back from here. Now, let's leave the dishes, take our glasses and the rest of the bottle and go into the drawing room. If you are a good boy, I might just tell you a story."

The expression of curiosity on his face was a picture, but I spun it all out, making sure that he was comfortable and taking ages to find some After Eights, which I knew he loved.

"Oh, for God's sake, get on with it!" he exploded.

"Sit down and listen and don't interrupt or you will hear nothing. It is all a big secret and nobody – but nobody – except Mr Pointer and I, knows what it is. As you are now a large part of my life, I will tell you."

I then proceeded to tell him the whole story. He already knew about my meeting with James and helping Lady Ruth; but when I came to the part about the portfolio of shares, Lady Ruth's death and my being left the use of Park Lodge, I could see that his surprise and curiosity was about as much as he could bear without commenting.

"I love that house," he said.

"Yes, so do I, and I think it would be nice if we both lived there instead of rattling around like two peas in a pod in this great place."

"Yes, that would be great," he spluttered.

This was good news to me because he was becoming a very large part of my life and very dear to me. I wanted so much for him to be part of any future that I planned.

"Now, settle down again and prepare yourself for part three," I said. "You know about James losing the herd in the foot-and-mouth epidemic, don't you?"

He nodded.

"Well, that was when everything started to go pear-shaped. Enormous debts and bankruptcy were looming on the horizon. It was then that Mr Pointer discovered that the shares which Lady Ruth had left me were worth a lot of money."

"So why didn't you help James with all this money?" he asked in surprise.

"The reason, if you would just let me finish, is that Mr Pointer could see all the money going down the same drain – all gone trying to keep the Hall and estate afloat. So he advised James to sell because the bank was going to foreclose. Pointer then sold the shares for me and bought the Hall in my name. James had all the money, settled his debts and got rid of all his worries in one fell swoop. We told him that it was an overseas investor who had bought the estate and that James could stay in the house until he came back to this country – which wasn't likely to be for a number of years. If James hadn't wanted to stay on here after the sale, then I had decided that we should pack up and go and live in Park Lodge. Fill my glass – this is all too much!"

He did so and I downed half of it.

"Hang on – not so fast. You'll be too pissed to finish the story."

I could tell that he was completely engrossed.

"Don't worry – it had a fairly happy ending for James. He wanted to move to Park Lodge, but, as the weeks went by, he got less able to do anything about it. He was tired, and happy to stay put. His money worries were over, and, although the illness had taken a firm hold by that time, we just spent the last months together having a wonderful time."

"What about his sisters? They must have been furious about the stocks and shares."

"They don't know anything about them. They were passed

to me as a gift, all perfectly legally, but you can see how his sisters would have stirred up trouble if they had known. Now, when I look back, I can see how wise Mr Pointer has been. He knew that James would be able to live out his last days with no worries at all. As far as possible, we were able to forget his illness and just live from day to day."

"So you own the estate, you bastard," he said with a shout.

"Yes, and if you don't behave yourself, I will turn you off it," I finished.

We sat for a while, both deep in our own thoughts. What had Barry made of all that I had told him? Should I go the whole hog and tell him Mr Pointer's revelations to me that morning? No, I would wait and see Mum first and ask about Lord Cameron. I would ring her tomorrow and go for Sunday lunch.

"You know, Barry, those last few months were wonderful. We had the Hall and gardens to ourselves and so we simply didn't do anything except eat and drink. In fact we did rather too much of the latter and were slightly merry – most of the time.

There was quite a lot of chat at the table, at least as far as Mum was concerned. Dad didn't say very much. She always wanted to know what had been happening at the Hall and how I was managing. Dad kept his own counsel and I caught him looking at me with a rather puzzled expression once or twice as if he didn't recognise the son he had reared. It occurred to me that I must have changed considerably from the boy of just a few years ago. I had learned much from James, and most of it concerned things that I don't suppose Dad ever thought of: architecture and paintings and more serious music. I now lived in a different world, so I could understand his bewilderment. He still called me 'boy', hardly ever addressing me as 'Robin'. Did he know something of the truth that Mr Pointer had revealed? He had always seemed distant too; there was never much warmth and never one hug in all my lifetime. Perhaps I was getting ahead of myself and reading things into his behaviour that didn't really exist. I decided to wait until he had gone to open up.

At twelve fifteen the bell rang and he was off. Some customers had come into the bar, so he would be busy until two thirty. As Mum cleared the table, I moved over to the china cabinet to look at the silver jug. I could see that the side facing me was quite heavily engraved with scrolls and other elaborate designs, including flowers on the base. As I looked at the jug, I noticed that beside it stood a silver photograph frame with a black-and-white print of Mother holding me in her arms. I could have been no more than a few months old at the time it was taken. I realised that she had been very beautiful and was in her 'Sunday best', as she would always say. The fact that it stood so close to the jug had more than a little significance. I could see why Lord Cameron had fallen for her. You always think of mums as mums, and not as beautiful women.

When she returned from the kitchen she noticed my interest in the cabinet and said, "What are you looking at?"

"I am just looking at your photograph, holding me. How old was I there?"

"Oh, about six months."

"You look a smasher. I bet the boys used to chase you."

"What do you mean?" She had an edge to her voice.

"You were so good-looking. I'll bet that is why the pub was always so busy."

"What are you on about? You're in a very strange mood, young man."

"No, just curious about the early days. I've never heard you talk much about them."

"Well, you were seldom here. No sooner had you left school than you went to college and then straight to the Hall."

I could see that she was uneasy about the drift of the conversation, but I pressed on: "Well, if it hadn't been the Hall, it would have been further away, in London or some other city, where there was a good hotel. So in fact you have seen more of me as things have turned out. Where is the key to the cabinet?"

"What do you want that for?"

Here goes: "I've never seen that claret jug properly. It's always facing the wrong way round. I've learned a bit about silver since being at the Hall. Where is the key?"

Reluctantly she said, "It's in the Toby jug, on the mantelpiece."

Quick as a shot, before she could change her mind, I extracted the key from the jug, my heart pumping wildly. Mum was looking flushed, but that might have been the effect of the very good burgundy I had brought from the cellars at the Hall to have with lunch. It was part of the softening-up plan I had hatched.

As I opened the cabinet I said, "I have always liked this jug more than anything else you have in here."

As I picked it up, I looked straight at her. She was more flushed than ever and she flopped into an armchair. Thank God Dad was busy in the bar.

As I turned it round in my hands, I read:

'Presented to Colour Sergeant A. M. Janney
By the N.C. Officers and Men of C Company
3rd Norfolk Regiment
3rd June 1895.'

I was silent for a few moments before looking at Mum and saying, "A. M. Janney? Is he related to the Janneys at the Hall? Is he part of James's family?"

I had her cornered, and she realised it. I had never heard her tell a lie.

She looked straight at me and said, "Yes, he was James's great-grandfather." I waited for her to continue, and after what seemed an eternity she said, "Lord Cameron gave it to me. I was very close to him once."

Tears were falling down her cheeks and I could feel my own welling up as I walked towards her and pulled her close to me.

"Yes, Mum, I know everything. I have just been given my inheritance. Lord Cameron left me £20,000."

"You must take the jug as well," she sobbed.

"Thank you, and you must have some of the money."

"No, I don't want anything. We are perfectly all right and have quite enough money in the bank to keep us going. That's why I've told Dad to stop working on the land. We have both worked so hard these last few years that we can manage now."

I was pleased to hear that. I had thought Dad had left his job on the estate because I was living there with James and was embarrassed, but, after all, it was Mum's insistence that had persuaded him to leave.

"You must keep calling him Dad, and think of Lord Cameron as 'Father'."

"Yes, I'll do that. Do you think Dad knows anything about all this?"

"I don't know – nothing has ever been said."

"Well, it can stay that way. Is there anything else I ought to know?"

"I suppose I ought to tell you how it all happened. You see, we met on one occasion at the Manor and he asked me if I could help at the Hall on the occasions when Lady Ruth had parties. This worked well for some time, but then she went to America for a holiday and I'm afraid we fell in love. I was so in love with him, but knew it couldn't go on; so I ended it. He begged me to go away with him, but I knew it would not last. How could it with the family, estate and all his friends to consider? How could he leave all that? It was only after we had parted that I found that I was pregnant. Of course, there was no going back. Dad always thought you were his, although during the last few years I have begun to have my doubts. We've been happy together and always will be, but it's not what you would think of as love."

I gave her another hug and kissed her on the forehead.

"There's no more to be said. Everything will be OK. How could I possibly mind? It's good that you had a real love."

I picked up the jug and looked closely at it. So many thoughts were going through my mind: Mum had experienced real love; I had fallen in love with my half-brother; I owned the Hall and the estate and was related to the rest of the family, who saw me as somebody who had stolen their home and possessions. If only they knew that I was more entitled to it than they were!

My mind was in turmoil. What to do next? I did not want to live at the Hall. I thought perhaps I should ring Simon, who seemed to have understood the relationship between James and myself. He had said that he would have bought the estate the first time if he had known it was available. He wanted his sons to have it to keep it in the family. I could move into Park Lodge, as James and I had intended, and retain the rights to walk the estate. When the renewal of the farm leases came up, they could have those as well, particularly if the boys wanted to farm. All this went through my head as I looked down at the jug and Mum waited for me to go on.

I kissed her and said, "Thank you for telling me and for the jug. I can now get on with my life, knowing what has happened and feeling good about it. I shall not stay at the Hall."

Seeing the puzzled look on her face, I went on: "You know Lady Ruth left me, for my lifetime, the use of Park Lodge?"

"No!" she said, obviously taken aback.

"Oh, I thought I told you when she died. There was so much going on at the time and then, later, with James being ill it must have slipped my mind. She was very grateful for the help I gave her – and the company. She was very lonely, you know, after Lord Cameron died. It does seem very generous, when I think about it; do you think she might have known about me? After all, I got a salary!"

I wondered, should I go on and tell her about the portfolio of shares? No, I thought there had been quite enough revelations for one day. I would keep it back for later.

Mum went on: "Lord Cameron might have told her, or perhaps something had been written down in case anything happened to him – as it did."

It crossed my mind that Mum must have been devastated when she heard Lord Cameron had been killed. No wonder she was furious with Dad when he told her so little after he had phoned the Hall. I remembered that she had phoned the Hall herself to get more details. She must have been going through hell, trying not to show her emotions. But then I remembered that Dad had cried, that Sunday morning. Surely he would not have done so if he had known that I was Lord Cameron's son. He would not have shed tears. He was so upset it was as if he was part of the family instead of just being one of the estate workers. How strange that all our fates seemed so entangled with the Janney family's!

"Well, Mum, all this really doesn't matter any more. All these things have happened for better or worse. We have our memories, most of them good; now we must just get on with the rest of our lives. I really must be going. Are you OK now?"

"Yes, dear, I'm feeling better now." And she wiped her eyes on her apron and straightened her shoulders.

"I must go. I promised to pick Barry up at the station. He's been up to Huddersfield to see his mother and his train gets in at three o'clock. I'll just be on time."

As I drove to the station I realised what a much better understanding we had of each other's lives. She knew that I had loved James and what unhappiness I must have suffered when he died. Now I knew of her loss after Lord Cameron's accident and felt closer to her. I decided, as I pulled into the station car park, that I would tell Barry the whole story just in case he learned it by accident when we visited Mum and Dad.

We embraced as he got off the train, and then we walked slowly down the platform to the car. I had taken to driving James's red sports car – just being in it made me feel closer to him.

As we pulled out of town, on to the country roads, I said, "Barry, I have something to tell you."

"Nothing bad, I hope."

"No, nothing bad, but I've just had lunch with Mum and she confirmed something Mr Pointer told me on Friday." And suddenly, feeling that all the pressures were gone, I gave him the complete story.

He didn't interrupt once, but when I had finished he said, "And how do you feel about it all?"

"I feel fine, I think. It has cleared up a lot of strange things that have happened over the last five years. Yes, I feel good. Now we must plan our future – you know I love you?"

"Yes, I know. And you know that I feel the same way." He hesitated. "I was just hoping that your love for James would not keep you from loving me."

"My love for James will always be with me – you know that – but it won't stop me from loving you. I've been blessed to have been loved twice so early in my life."

We swung into the driveway, and as we neared the front entrance Bella came bounding up with her usual boisterous welcome. We spent the evening quietly, quite comfortable in each other's company.

On Monday morning, on the stroke of nine, I phoned Simon.

"Good morning. Calthorpe Benny Associates," a brisk young lady's voice answered.

Calthorpe Benny were stockbrokers and Simon was the senior partner. They had made a great deal of money on the stock market during the last few years. Simon was also a Lloyd's Name, so money seemed no problem.

"Good morning. Can I speak to Sir Simon Calthorpe, please?"

"Just one moment. Who shall I say is calling?"

"Robin Partner."

"Thank you."

Simon came on the line: "Hello, Robin. It's good to hear from you. How can I help?"

"Good morning, Simon. I'm wondering if we can get together as soon as possible. It's about the estate."

"Yes, what about the estate?"

"Well, I think it is coming on the market again and I know you were interested in the past."

"Look – I'm free on Thursday. I can get a flight from Edinburgh. I'll call you back as soon as I have the time."

"Look, Simon – if you are free on Friday as well, stay overnight. I leave that up to you. Bring Daphne as well if you wish."

"I'm not sure about that, but I'll ask her and let you know. Bye."

Having got that side of things going, I picked up the receiver and phoned Mr Pointer.

"Hello, Mr Pointer. Robin here."

"Hello, Robin. I was just thinking about you. Are you bearing up under all that news I gave you on Friday?"

"Yes, thank you. I had a few words with Mum over the weekend. Once she got over her surprise, I think she was relieved to be able to tell me herself."

"Well, I'm pleased to hear it. How can I help you?"

"Mr Pointer, I need to speak to you as soon as possible. I think it would be best over lunch, but I don't have a great deal of time. Can you make it this week? It has to be sorted out before Thursday."

"Well, I'm free for lunch on Wednesday. Shall I come over to you?"

"Yes, of course. Can you bring all my papers? I've decided not to stay at the Hall and I have spoken to Simon Calthorpe, who, I know, wants the estate for Angus and Frazer. He is flying down on Thursday."

'Yes, yes, I'll get them all together and bring them over on Wednesday. Will eleven o'clock be suitable?"

"Perfect. It will give us plenty of time before a one-o'clock lunch. I look forward to seeing you then."

And so the wheels were set in motion. Now that the decision was made, how good it would be to get it all wrapped up! "Positive mental attitude," as James always said.

When Wednesday arrived, and knowing Mr Pointer's unfailing punctuality, I had everything prepared. The roast duck and the pudding were doing nicely in the Aga. The day before the weather had been so bright and fine that I had taken one of James's guns and, with Bella, had walked across the water meadows. The duck population had risen alarmingly after Lord Cameron died. James had not kept up the shoots and when Dad, as gamekeeper, had left as well, there had been a significant increase in all the game. At least I had reduced the population by a couple of brace – one of which was in the oven, and the other hanging in the larder for Simon.

Right on the first stroke of eleven, by the grandfather clock in the hall, Bella started leaping about. She had heard Mr Pointer's car on the gravel followed shortly by the bell.

"Morning, my boy – lovely morning."

"Good morning, Mr Pointer. Yes, it is. I'm rather hoping it's going to keep up for the rest of the week. It will be more pleasant for Simon. Come on through to the drawing room. Sherry or wine?"

"Thank you. A nice drop of sherry would go down a treat."

As we sat down, Barry appeared in the doorway.

"Good morning, Mr Pointer. Robin, I'll have lunch ready for one o'clock. That should give you plenty of time."

"Hello, Barry," said the old man. "I can tell from the aroma that you have something special in the oven!"

"Wait and see," said Barry with a grin, and off he went.

"I have really thought about all this, Mr Pointer. I know you said I was just as entitled to live here as anyone else, but we've talked it over and decided that we don't want all this round our necks. We are not really into farming and the Hall without the farms seems a little pointless. In any case, why spend enormous sums of money keeping up this place if we only use a tiny fraction of it? No, we would rather live in Park Lodge. That way, we shall still be living on the estate, which we both love. If Angus or Frazer gets married and lives here, well, that would be a bonus."

"And what if Simon and Daphne want to live here? Would that cause any problems?"

"I can't see why it should. If they want to invite us over for drinks, well, fine; if not, it won't matter one iota. We shall keep the rights to walk over the estate and I am going to take all the things that I know James loved and set them up in Park Lodge."

Pointer looked relieved and said, "Well, that all sounds fine."

I know he had been concerned about my relationship with the family, and I could tell from his expression that he still had one or two reservations.

"Are you going to tell Daphne that you are her half-brother?"

"Yes. That way, if we were living at Park Lodge, they would know that I have a right to be there. I also intend to keep my shooting rights – even though I don't go out very much. That way I shall feel closer to James."

"Yes, I can see that. Now all I need to know is how much you want for the place."

"I'm prepared to take your advice, as always, Mr Pointer. Simon wants it, and with you doing all the paperwork we shall not need an estate agent. That will not only save money, but also avoid publicity locally. Nobody really needs to know, but you know what villages are!"

"I've been giving the matter a deal of thought, Robin. If you include the farms, which are bringing in reasonable rents, the Hall and the rest of the estate, plus a bit of profit to cover the expenditure you have had, I think you should ask £200,000. I have no idea what to add on for any furniture, pictures and so on that you may be leaving; you would have to ask an auctioneer to take care of that for you."

I thought for a moment before saying, "We are going to take what we want to furnish Park Lodge as we would like it to be. We shall need some more from the Hall and what we move out of the lodge to furnish another property that we might buy in town. We will purchase a house either on the coast or in the town so that we are settled before doing anything else."

"That is a splendid idea. At least you will have two furnished homes, and then you can invest the rest of your capital in shares, or some enterprise or whatever, without worrying."

"Yes, we thought it might be a good idea to have a restaurant or a gallery of some kind. Either would keep us occupied without working for anybody else."

"I agree with all you say, my boy. Just make sure that you keep some money in property; it will never let you down."

We heard Barry shout from the hallway, "Lunch is ready."

As we got to our feet, I smiled at him and said, "Whatever happens, we will still have some good lunches together at Park Lodge. I'll take the rest of the wine from the cellar to keep us going."

The old man chuckled as he made his way to the dining room.

When he had left and we were in the kitchen washing the dishes, I said to Barry, "I'm glad that's all settled; it was going to be a bit difficult continuing to run the Hall and the estate. The only thing I shall miss is the swimming pool, but that will only be in the winter."

"Why only the winter?" Barry asked.

"Because in the summertime James and I always used to swim in the river, just below the willow trees in the south meadow. The water is always crystal-clear and nobody could see us. We spent many afternoons and evenings swimming in our birthday suits. We can still swim there, but with people living in the Hall we might have to wear swimming trunks," I laughed.

"You never mentioned that to me," he pouted.

"I guess there are lots of things that will come out in the next few years that were things we just did naturally and not the sort of things you tell anybody about."

He held my face in his soapy hands and kissed me. "Yes, I know," he said, and went back to the washing-up.

That evening, Simon rang to say that they would be arriving around eleven thirty on the following morning. Daphne had decided to come with him after all. I got the impression from Simon that she knew she had been rude on the day of the funeral and, as the boys had already been to stay, she wanted to patch things up between us. Or was that wishful thinking on my part? I hoped that I had not misjudged the situation, because I had decided to tell her that I was her half-brother.

I had planned another game pie for lunch. It was already in the oven with a dish of roasting vegetables. The rest of the meal was prepared so that there would be nothing to distract us once we started to talk. Barry had said that it would be better if he made himself scarce and so had gone to visit some of his friends in town. I had the champagne on ice – that should help to calm a few nerves, I thought. I'd already had a glassful myself when I heard the taxi on the driveway.

"Good morning, Daphne and Simon. I hope you had a good flight."

"Yes," she answered, coming up the steps and kissing me on both cheeks, which was a good sign.

Simon took up the conversation, anxious that there should be no awkward lull: "Yes, the flight was on time – not a single delay. That's what always upsets me – the little things that go wrong when I fly down to London each week."

"Come on in. The champagne is in the ice bucket."

How I seemed to have got used to this lifestyle! I was no longer the callow boy that had been so fearful of meeting James's sisters all those years ago.

"Champagne," Daphne said, smiling, "just like old times."

I could see her eyes taking in every detail of the house. Perhaps she had just come to check me out. Then I remembered that she had, after all, been brought up there – that all her roots were there. I knew she must miss the old place.

"Well, I'm afraid there isn't much left in the cellar – just a few bottles of port. James so liked his champagne that that was all he drank in the last few years." I desperately wanted to change the subject as I could feel myself getting tearful.

Simon was in a very quiet mood, enjoying his champagne. He had moved over to the great sash windows to look out across the parkland.

"What are you going to do with all the furniture and the pictures when you move out?" Daphne asked.

The edge to her voice reinforced my conviction that Daphne had arrived with an agenda of her own. I was suddenly relieved that they were not staying, but leaving by the evening flight.

"I'm not sure," I shrugged. "It depends a lot on who buys it."

"We are going to buy it," she snapped.

"Just hold your horses, Daphne. Let's wait and see what Robin has to say first."

He had walked back towards the fireplace as he spoke.

'If she's going to be as rude as that, the price goes up another thousand for every bit of bitchiness,' I thought to myself.

"Let's top up our glasses and take a seat by the fire. I will tell you a story that may come as something of a surprise, and then I'll leave you both to it whilst I get the lunch ready and you can talk it over between yourselves."

I stood with my back to them, looking into the fire as they settled down on the settee. I thought I could see both Lady Ruth's and James's faces in the flames. Were they there in the room for me?

"As you both know," I said, still gazing into the flames, "I helped your mother and she thanked me by leaving me the use of Park Lodge. I know how she loved that house and always wanted it to be used. My intention is to live there and to take what furniture and pictures I need there. When the house comes back to your boys, the furniture will come with it. It would be nice for them to have the family portraits with the house."

I did not look at them as I moved from the fireplace to the window. When I turned, with the light behind me, I could see that Daphne's face was contorted with anger. She now knew that I was taking the portraits.

I paused and then continued: "Whilst she was alive, Lady Ruth gave me a portfolio of shares, which had come to her, at the time of her marriage, from her mother. She told me that they were for me to do with as I wished, but also to help James if he had any problems. As you know, the farms were not doing very well before the foot-and-mouth disaster made it ten times worse, and then the house had to be reroofed at considerable expense. Together, all this nearly wiped James out."

Before I could continue, Daphne exclaimed, "Well, why didn't you use the money from Mother's stocks and shares to save him?"

I waited a moment before replying. Then, glancing across at Simon, I said, "Everything that has been done has been carried out on the advice of the Janney family's solicitor, Mr Pointer. It was he who recommended that I sell the shares – first to acquire the farms, and later the Hall and parkland. He, at least, knew that I had James's best interests at heart. He knew that if I just handed the money to James it would, in time, just dwindle away on the upkeep of the estate and then he would be back to square one. You must remember that the bank held the deeds of the property against his borrowings. With the bequests that Lord and Lady Janney (your mother and father) made at the time of their deaths, they left James with precious little money to keep going. Death duties took what little he had, so he was forced to borrow."

I could see that her mind was working overtime, but before she could interrupt I continued: "With the money from the shares safely banked, your solicitor advised James to sell because the bank was now seriously concerned and was pressing for repayment of the loan. He advised that, once the Hall was sold, we should move into Park Lodge – something that James was very keen to do. You must remember that James was very ill at this time and viewed the prospect of being free from financial worries with a great deal of relief. Your mother's shares included some Poseidon stock – I think an Australian mining company—"

Before I could continue, Simon interrupted: "Poseidon? They certainly took off at that time. I wonder who advised her to buy those?"

"You will never have to look much further than Mr Pointer. He always had the family's best interests at heart. But you're right; by the time he had finished selling them there was sufficient for me to buy the estate. Mr Pointer advised me to tell James that it had been sold to an overseas investor. He told James that he would not need the property for some years and that James could have the use of it at a nominal rent provided he kept up the appearance of the house and grounds." I took another large gulp of champagne, believing that it was giving me the courage to tell my story. "This way we were able to make James happy and comfortable. After he had paid off the thirty-odd thousand pounds that was owed, he had plenty of money to enjoy what was left of his life."

"So you own the estate!" Daphne exploded.

Simon shouted, "Why don't you be quiet and let Robin finish what he has to tell us?"

But she wouldn't be silenced: "I might have known, after you got in with Mother. Veronica always said that you were up to something."

I knew that this had to be the moment to drop the bombshell: "Daphne, I know you keep your head firmly rooted in the sand, but if you had been just a little more aware of what was going on around you and not so caught up with Veronica's viciousness, you might have guessed that James and I loved each other and that I loved Lady Ruth. That is why she gave me the shares, so that I could help James. But there is more."

I paused and took a deep breath before saying, "On my

twenty-first birthday, I inherited £20,000 from your father, Lord Cameron. With it came a letter informing me that I was his son. So you see, Daphne, by the greatest irony, you are my half-sister!"

She sat with her mouth wide open, speechless with shock. I had finally silenced her.

Simon said gently, "Daphne, I told you to listen to what Robin had to say. I always had the feeling that there was something more than just friendship between Robin and your mother." He turned to me: "Robin, may I ask if Lady Ruth knew the truth of the matter?"

"I don't really know," I replied, "but she knew that I loved James and would always take care of him."

"Yes, and thank you for doing so," he said graciously. Still Daphne said nothing, so Simon continued: "Have you spoken with your mother?"

"Yes, we have talked it all through. She was, I believe, greatly relieved that I had been told. I hope that I can rely on you both to keep all this between the three of us?"

"Daphne, do you hear that? Not one word to Veronica," Simon said sharply.

"Yes, I understand," she replied.

I topped up their glasses once more. It was my intention to finish this before lunch, so I plunged in and said, "I have had the estate valued at £220,000 and I have decided to sell whether you buy it or not. After I have removed such items of furniture that I need, the rest will go to Angus and Frazer."

Almost before I could finish, and certainly before Daphne could utter a single word, Simon said, "Robin, I will buy it, at the price you mention, for the boys. I will sign whatever is necessary as soon as the papers can be drawn up. The funds are available as soon as that is done. Frazer is going to Australia with his girlfriend for a few years, but Angus has become very interested in this newfangled organic gardening. I think the large walled garden and the three meadows adjoining would be ideal. He's been doing a course at an agricultural college on organic horticulture and is very serious about it."

Simon didn't know it, but Angus had already told me all this earlier in the year when he was staying. It would be a great bonus to have him nearby – I had become very fond of him and, I believe, he of me.

"That's settled, then." I shook Simon's hand. "The land hasn't had anything on it except sheep and cows, and it was always good old-fashioned manure in the garden. It should all be well suited to organic vegetables. I'll be able to pop over the fence and get them fresh."

I smiled at them both, but Daphne still sat with her head lowered, deep in thought. Simon returned my smile and the expression on his face told me to be patient and she would come round.

"Give me ten minutes, and then come through to the dining room for lunch," I told them.

"Robin, do you mind if I skip lunch? I'm really not feeling very hungry," she murmured.

"No problem," I replied. "If you need anything later, you know where everything is in the kitchen. There have been no changes there." And I left them to it.

When they were on their own, Daphne blurted out, "How could he have got everything?"

"Well, he did love James, and James was mighty fond of him for several years. You know your mother was very fond of him and he certainly looked after them both."

"I know, but *everything*!"

"Look, Daphne – if he had not arranged things as he did, we might not be sitting here and we would certainly not be in a position to be able to buy the estate. As it is, most of the family furniture and pictures will be coming back to the boys. On reflection, I think we have come out of this better than we could possibly have hoped."

"Yes, I know, but—"

"No buts. He is your half-brother, and perhaps he is more entitled to it all than you think. He ends up with the value of the shares your mother wanted him to have, and we end up with your family home to pass to the boys. Now, let it all be and let's carry on properly. He is going to be living on the estate, and remember that the boys like him very much. He has been kind to them. Now I am going to have some lunch. Don't drink too much whilst I'm gone." And he left her to her thoughts.

Over lunch, I told Simon of my intention to keep the right to walk the estate as well as the shooting. I told him that the farms were leased out to good tenants at reasonable rents. All that didn't worry him one jot. He told me he could think about that when Frazer returned from Australia. If the boy wanted to run the farms, he could do so. There was plenty of land for Angus's little enterprise.

By the time we had finished lunch I knew that everything was in place. Barry and I had the capital to start afresh; we also had Park Lodge and all its connections to James and Lady Ruth, and we could buy our little house by the sea.

The sea is crashing on the shore
And the clouds are blotting out my North Star.
As the clock strikes midnight
The New Millennium has dawned.

I must get back. Barry is waiting and the champagne is on ice.
The memories of my North Star will be with me forever.